KꓬY

Please return or renew this item before the latest date shown below

D1313254

Renewals can be made

by internet	www.fifedirect.org.uk/libraries
in person	at any library in Fife
by phone	08451 55 00 66

Fife 洸
COUNCIL

Thank you for using your library

Travels with My Heart

The Essential Guide for Travellers with Heart Conditions

Robin Liston

Foreword by
Ranulf Fiennes

Illustrations by Georgie Birkett

Matador
9 De Montfort Mews
Leicester LE1 7FW, UK
Tel: (+44) 116 255 9311 / 9312
Email: books@troubador.co.uk
Web: www.troubador.co.uk/matador

ISBN 978-1905886-883

Typeset in 11pt Bembo by Troubador Publishing Ltd, Leicester, UK
Printed in the UK by The Cromwell Press Ltd, Trowbridge, Wilts, UK

Matador is an imprint of Troubador Publishing Ltd

To Rebecca and Chris, Vicky and Chris, Issy and Eliza

Contents

PART THREE – HEART SEARCHING

Foreword

by Ranulph Fiennnes

I was boarding a flight at Bristol Airport en route to Edinburgh in June 2003, when I suddenly collapsed with a heart attack. I was lucky to have the attack before the flight took off and also extremely lucky that a mobile defibrillating unit and the expert assistance of the Blue Watch of the Bristol Airport Fire Station were immediately on the scene.

With the help of a double bypass operation, and the expertise and care of the staff at Bristol Royal Infirmary, I was soon on the road to fitness again, and four months later, I managed to complete seven marathons in seven continents in seven days in aid of the British Heart Foundation.

Admittedly my expeditions over the years have kept me perhaps fitter than most people of 63, but there is no doubt that one of the quickest ways to recover from a heart attack is to regain a good level of physical and mental strength. In my view, there is no better way of doing this than undertaking some adventurous activities, particularly those involving travel.

Therefore I was very pleased to see the publication of *Travels with My Heart*, the first comprehensive guide for travellers with heart conditions. The guide is an antidote to the shock and depression that often follows a cardiac incident, but while written in a light-hearted way, it is deadly serious about the value of adventurous and unusual travel as a route to mental and physical recovery.

I recommend it to all those with cardiac problems, as well as to their family and friends. The book is packed with travel and health information, plus some amusing descriptions of the author's own travel adventures after having a heart attack of his own in 2004.

Perhaps a seven-marathon odyssey might be overdoing it for most people recovering from heart conditions, but this book will act as a valuable road map for those who may currently feel depressed and listless as a result of their illness, and are looking for a way forward in order to get their lives back on track.

Congratulations on a great book and great travels. May you 'tick' for a very long while!

Ranulph Fiennes is a British explorer and holder of several endurance records including being the first man to visit both North and South poles by land and to cross the Antarctic Continent unsupported. He recently climbed the north face of the Eiger in order to raise money for Marie Curie Cancer Care.

Acknowledgements

There are many people who have encouraged me in this project. I am particularly grateful to Madeleine Guppy for exerting consistent but gentle pressure on me to write the book in the first place; Sharon Robinson, Specialist Cardiac Rehabilitation Nurse at the Whittington Hospital in North London, who not only helped to put me back on my feet, but read the manuscript and made many helpful comments; John Robinson and Geoff Watkins who gave me invaluable help on the walking section; Phil Turner for his contribution on rowing down the Thames; Dr John Cooper, Head of Corporate Occcupational Health aat Unilever, Christine McDermott and Val West who all read the first draft and put me straight on matters medical and/or grammatical; Hywel Evans my proof reader; Jeremy Thompson, my publisher; Paul and Larry Goodyer of Nomad Travel for advice on keeping fit while travelling; and Ranulph Fiennes, who kindly wrote the foreword to the book and is an inspiration to anyone recovering from a heart condition. Thanks also go to Veronica Robinson, Val Gerdes and Judy Turner who looked after me in the first few weeks after my heart attack and didn't allow me to feel sorry for myself.

Part One

Lift Up Your Heart

Chapter 1

Why Travel is Good for your Heart

My heart aches, and a drowsy numbness pains
My sense, as though of hemlock I had drunk

My knowledge of poetry is minimal. However I learned these lines
by John Keats at school and for some reason, they kept going
through my head as I lay in the coronary care unit of a small hospital,
240 miles from home.

As so often with traumatic moments in your life, the day had
started quite unremarkably. I was visiting my family in North
Yorkshire and had just spent a welcome twenty minutes luxuriating
in the bath. As I got out, I felt a peculiar pain across my chest and a
nauseous sensation.

After ten minutes the pain subsided, so I got dressed, had
breakfast and finished off some pressing work. I then went down the
road to visit a relative. I was drinking a cup of coffee with him when
the pain came back like a tornado and sweat started pouring down
my neck.

After that, I remember very little until I found myself lying on a
trolley in A&E with a very young-looking doctor standing over me,
pronouncing that I had had a moderately serious heart attack; or to
put it in technical terms, an *inferior myocardial infarction with ST
elevation*.

Just how serious this might be only began to dawn on me when
my two daughters turned up later that day – one lives in London and
the other near Oxford. Both had made a 240-mile journey to check
that I was still breathing. My eldest daughter even had the smaller of
my two granddaughters in tow.

I was pleased that they had gone to such trouble for their dad, but at the same time fearful that they had thought it necessary.

Both my father and grandfather had died from heart problems. I suppose, therefore, that I might subconsciously have suspected that one day my heart was likely to cut up rough too. However I had never really given it much thought, despite my notorious tendency to hypochondria. Perhaps I simply chose to ignore the fact that according the latest statistics from the **British Heart Foundation**, coronary heart disease (CHD) is still the UK's single biggest killer, claiming nearly 117,000 lives each year.

Over the years I had convinced myself that I had every type of cancer known to man, not to mention HIV and a brain tumour. But even the most diligent doctors, not to mention several expensive but questionable alternative therapists, had failed to find anything much wrong. Yet strangely I had never found room for a heart attack in my catalogue of imagined maladies.

My knowledge of the workings of the body has always been sketchy, not helped by a lack of any science 'O' levels. I had certainly spent plenty of time in hospital, but this was mainly due to the medical problems of other members of my family. I would qualify for a PhD in hospital visiting if such a degree existed, and I have picked up bits of knowledge relating to my family's many and varied ailments. However, at this time, I was woefully ignorant of most things medical and had very little understanding of heart attacks or my chances of a full recovery.

Suffering from any type of heart condition is a life-changing experience. I used to own a series of cars whose engines had a habit of packing up at crucial moments. Even after I had spent a fortune on repairs, I never felt entirely confident that they would not break down again on a dark wet night in the middle of nowhere.

After a heart operation or heart attack, most people feel like I did about my dodgy cars. You are never quite sure when your heart is going to start malfunctioning again. Therefore, apart from the obvious need to implement a fitness regime, the most important thing is to rebuild up confidence in your own body.

Although I was one of the lucky ones who, at least for the moment, had given the Grim Reaper the brush-off, I had received a clear warning that I must clean up my act, lose weight, get plenty of exercise and turn myself into a model squeaky-clean citizen.

So as soon as I got home from hospital, I decided that I was not going to allow myself to be treated with kid gloves or be wrapped in cotton wool. Anyway, I soon hit a point when I was no longer the centre of attention yet I still didn't feel confident with my own body or about the future. This seemed to be the moment when I needed to start planning a get-fit strategy.

Can you remember learning to swim? I was taught by a ferocious ex-army physical fitness instructor who made us attempt to swim up and down an unheated open-air pool, supported only by a sling on a pole. Now I really hated swimming, but I will never forget the day when I realised that the coach was dangling the sling along the bottom of the pool and it was no longer supporting me – yet I was still afloat.

In a sense, recovering from heart surgery or a heart attack is a not dissimilar experience. At first you feel secure in hospital with checks every few minutes and the knowledge that there is expert care on hand. When you get home, hopefully you will have the support of friends and/or family. Additionally, many hospitals have good post-coronary care programmes which certainly help you through the first few months. I would like to mention in particular the one run by Sharon Robinson at the Whittington Hospital in North London, which certainly did an enormous amount to get me back on my feet.

However, after that it's mainly down to you and your belief that you can swim on your own and that there's life in the old dog yet.

I realised straight away that my swim-not-sink strategy would have to include an element of travel, simply because I love travelling almost more than anything. I first got the bug as a child when my tri-lingual mother would organise epic car journeys across Europe each summer. My father couldn't drive, but my mother thought nothing of setting off with three children in the back of our two-tone green Humber Hawk. One year we visited ten countries in three weeks and there was always the odd mishap, including my father breaking his toe on a picnic table and my older sister throwing up over a gendarme in Paris.

When I was growing up, my father travelled abroad a great deal and would bring home piles of airline timetables from everywhere he visited. These were my prized possessions, all carefully filed alphabetically and consulted on a daily basis. I was thrilled when he brought home a massive *ABC Airways Guide* which I got to know intimately. He would often set me complicated routes and deadlines, for which I would have to produce detailed itineraries.

However 45 years on, I was now involved in travel planning of a different sort. I had to find travel 'experiences' that would involve some reasonably hard physical exercise, because I had learned one medical fact: your heart needs to be given a reasonable work-out most days if you are going to live to a decent old age.

Don't get me wrong. I don't particularly like physical exercise and I have never had a desire to be a lumberjack, or pull a large truck along with my teeth. But if I had to choose between chopping down some trees in an attractive away-from-home environment, or spending sixty minutes daily on a treadmill at the local Fitness-a-Go-Go club, then it was a no-brainer. It was the adventure holiday for me.

So I started hunting for interesting travel challenges – challenges that would help me to recover and rebuild confidence in my body and its ability to see me well into the future. Challenges that would lead to interesting adventures and much better tales to tell friends and family than the fifteenth reprise of 'the day I nearly died'.

I accept that it is not possible for everyone with a heart problem to use travel as a route to recovery. For lots of reasons, it may not be practical to take off into the blue yonder. Perhaps you feel fit enough to go back to work and don't dare take any more time off. You may well be short of cash, particularly if you have been dependent on sickness benefit, or have only a modest pension to live on – you may also be too ill to travel.

If you are a youngish victim, you may have all sorts of financial and work problems to sort out, and possibly a young family to cope with. If you are older, you may find yourself suddenly in enforced retirement. If you are already retired, you may be unable (or at least think you are unable) to do all the things you planned to do during your 'third age', as the French so elegantly describe the over-60s.

However, I came to the conclusion that it would be possible for most people with heart conditions and modest financial resources to take up at least one travel-related challenge and I therefore started assembling a mass of information and advice. You will find the results in this book.

Living up to the challenge

Let's look on the bright side. 2.6 million UK citizens with heart problems have given death the slip for the time being. They have escaped the coronary care unit in one piece, but there are still several challenges to face and problems to overcome.

I should emphasis from the outset that this book is *not* about illnesses of the heart or how to overcome them. After all, do you really want to learn about coronary disease from someone who could not even pass biology O level?

Nor is it, you will be relieved to know, the rambling memoirs of a coronary victim. The author John Updike claimed that a healthy male adult bore consumes each year, one and half times his own weight in other people's patience. A typical unhealthy male will consume far more than this. Unlike women, who usually bear pain in stoical silence, men tend to share theirs liberally and without great discrimination.

Incidentally, there is even now a device, developed at the Massachusetts Institute of Technology, that can tell if you are boring. The Emotional Intelligence Prosthetic consists of a small camera attached to a pair of glasses connected to a hand-held computer. If the wearer fails to engage his or her listener's attention, the computer, loaded with image-recognition software, vibrates. Though designed for people with autism, it sounds perfect for heart problem bores too.

I didn't think it would be particularly helpful either to write one of those inspirational books about patients who have suffered from heart problems but have overcome their disabilities to become superheroes with the honourable exception of Ranulph Fiennes. You know the sort of thing: 50-year old struck down by heart disease. Goes on to win 15 Olympic gold medals while solving the problem of Third World debt, writing a Booker Prize-winning novel, conducting the Berlin Philharmonic Orchestra to rapturous applause, and adopting 13 Bosnian orphans.

Maxwell "Max" Woosnam (1892-1965) was the sort of person I am talking about. He was a Wimbledon tennis champion and captain of the British Davis Cup team, an Olympic gold medallist, captain of Manchester City and the England football team, scored a century at Lords, got a maximum 147 break in snooker and won a table tennis game against Charlie Chaplin, using a butter knife rather than a bat. On top of this, he was a good businessman and a member of the board of ICI.

Let's face it: most of us are no Max Woosnams. We were fairly ordinary souls before our heart problems. Why should we suddenly expect to become extraordinary just because we have acquired a dicky ticker?

However, whatever you do, don't fall into the trap of a man in his eighties whom I used to visit. He had had a triple coronary bypass in his early fifties and decided that he was going to die at any moment. He had become agoraphobic, rarely leaving home again, and utterly obsessed with his heart which, in reality, had kicked back into passable service many years before. It took him nearly 30 years to die and when he finally turned up his toes, it was mainly due to three decades of inactivity.

I have deliberately made no assumptions about the typical reader of this book. Heart disease does not discriminate. You may be male or female, straight or gay, live with a spouse or partner, or on your own; you may still live with one or both parents, or in some sort of community. You may be a teenager or a pensioner, a manual worker or a City high-flyer.

Thus I have tried ensure that every travel activity described in this book is equally feasible for single people, couples, friends and family groups. Obviously your economic and health circumstances will dictate what you can do, but hopefully you will find something to suit your taste, needs and pocket within this book.

I have also tried to be realistic. There are clearly some danger zones like Bolivia and Peru, which (terrorists and drug dealers aside) are at a very high altitude, or places like Mexico City, which is both very high and extremely polluted, thereby putting you at unnecessary risk.

The only activity to which I have devoted a whole chapter is walking, because it is as good as it gets as far as your heart is concerned, and it is possible to have rambling holidays or days out on a very modest budget. Furthermore, there are very few heart conditions that would preclude gentle walking, and as many parts of the UK are perfect for rambling and hiking, you will not have to face long and potentially stressful overseas journeys.

I have also taken diet into consideration and have produced a whirlwind tour of different cuisines you will find around the world, with some words of warning about those countries whose food might put a strain on your heart, not to mention your digestion. I can remember working in Northern Ireland during the 1970s and 1980s, at a time when it seemed that the only known cooking technique was deep frying everything and anything in lard. As I had a dodgy gall bladder – whose main function is to collect and concentrate the bile that aids the digestion of fats – you can imagine that I had a pretty rotten time.

I have also looked at the problems of obtaining medical insurance. Many travel insurance companies do not want to cover people with pre-existing medical conditions and others charge unreasonably high premiums for doing so.

Fortunately, I have found a few companies that specialise in travel insurance for people with pre-existing medical conditions. They are particularly sympathetic to travellers with heart problems and treat them extremely fairly and with consideration.

I have also sought some expert advice on the physical impact of air travel on those of us who suffer from heart problems. So while this book encourages you to be adventurous, it does not egg you on to acts of gross irresponsibility.

We will get into some basic 'stay healthy' rules later, but it is worth bearing in mind that the combination of stress and an increase in altitude – with the resulting decrease in oxygen level – is often the precipitating factor in airborne heart attacks. So the best advice I have been given, and must pass on to you, is to get a good medical check-up before you set off on your travels.

A useful tip is to allow yourself plenty of time both for preparing for the trip and actually getting to your point of departure. Fortunately I have a built-in tendency to be early, borne of innate pessimism. Unlike my more optimistic friends who don't believe that they will ever get caught in a traffic jam on the M25, or get stuck on a recalcitrant underground train, I always assume that it will definitely happen to me, with the result that I have only very occasionally missed a plane, train or ferry. Unfortunately the recently introduced security restrictions at airports are likely to add to your stress, particularly as airlines now strongly advise you not to arrive too early, in order to avoid congestion in the departure terminals.

Another basic rule is to avoid high-altitude destinations, or at least travel to them gradually. The altitude exposure of commercial air travel cannot be avoided, but is usually limited to the equivalent of 5,000 to 8,000 feet. Due to slower blood circulation and the fact that many are on diuretics, heart patients are more prone to blood clots. In the dehydrating atmosphere and with the diminished scope for physical activity of air travel, this becomes more of a problem. Drinking lots of fluids, stretching out where possible and frequent movement about the plane are important in preventing this.

Off-beat choices

Shortly after my heart attack, I was invited to a wedding anniversary celebration in Slovakia. It involved a flight to Bratislava and a four-hour train journey, followed by two days of fairly solid celebrations. I was very nervous about travelling and carefully read up about Slovakian hospitals and medical services. I was somewhat comforted when I discovered that the town I was visiting had a small airport which happened to be the main base for air ambulances. Furthermore, Vienna was only a 20-minute flight away so I felt that it was worth taking the risk.

I did feel a bit under the weather on a train travelling between Popgrad and Bratislava, and the Slovak baggage handlers burrowed through my suitcase. However I got home in one piece and felt a lot more confident about life afterwards.

Then a few days later, I received an email about a cheap learn-to-sail holiday in the Ionian Islands in North West Greece. I hadn't sailed since I was 18, and it all sounded quite strenuous. However the sailing school assured me that my physical condition was no problem and that they were sure it would be good for me.

A week of throwing myself around a 35ft French-built sailing boat with three gung-ho lads from Wolverhampton who I had never met before in my life, proved to be a great morale booster. Unexpectedly, I thoroughly enjoyed myself, even on the night when I got soaked in my bunk because the boat leaked during a vicious storm. I suspect that I will always be a very mediocre sailor, but I might make a passably useful crew member if I stick at it.

Soon after, I spent a weekend on an activity break with the National Trust. For £37, anyone can join a weekend working party and carry out a variety of tasks from coppicing and fence-building to planting heather and installing 'kissing gates' to conform to health and safety regulations. In exchange for your money and labour, you get some fairly primitive accommodation and variable food, but you meet lots of interesting and unusual people. For example, there was one volunteer in her twenties with a passion for ladies' corsets.

In addition to these adventures, I have spent a month working on conservation projects in Australia and worked in the mountains of North West Spain with high-powered Spaniards who had signed up for an 'immersion' course in English.

New experiences

With each new experience, I have taken one further step to recovery. I have learned new skills, seen different places and gradually felt better about myself than I did before I fell ill. In other words, the process of recovery has been a window into new worlds and experiences.

I have tried to describe these activities and trips in such a way that will make you want to try some of them – or something similar – yourself. But let's be clear that I am not trying to prove what a clever or brave chap I am. On the contrary, I am a very ordinary soul with very limited physical skills, and I am certainly not particularly brave.

As you will see, these trips have varied wildly in terms of location, climate, activity, adventurousness and strenuousness. Some will not be suitable for people with serious heart conditions, and you should always alert the organisers of any trip or activity you undertake to your state of health, level of fitness and any other special considerations or requirements you might have.

The accounts of these trips do not propose a particular programme of activities (although, if you fancy trying any of them, full details for all are to be found in Part 3) and I am not suggesting that you do all of them. Rather, Part 2 is an unashamedly personal account of some of the things I have enjoyed doing since my heart attack – some of the things that have helped me back to fitness. I hope these 'postcards' from close, and not-so-close, to home will show that there is life after a heart attack and that a heart condition is no obstacle to seeing a bit of the world, doing what you enjoy and opening the door to all manner of new experiences. Their aim is to inspire rather than to instruct.

If my experience encourages you to stretch yourself a bit, then my purpose will have been achieved. As a lifelong sloth, I used to have pinned on my wall a quote from the great car manufacturer Henry Ford: 'Exercise is bunk. If you are healthy you don't need it. If you are sick, you shouldn't take it'. That dubious comic Les Dawson had a great one-liner: 'Lazy? He used to ride his bike over cobblestones to knock the ash off his ciggie'. Well, that was me before my heart attack.

I now realise – hopefully in the nick of time – how wrong Henry Ford was. I prefer the dictum of Ted Kaptchuk, Assistant Professor at Harvard Medical School, that 'health is an episode between two illnesses'. My aim is to make that episode as long as possible.

I should stress at the outset that, although much of the information in this book has been taken from medically sound sources, and drawn from the literature and advice routinely disseminated to heart patients, I am not a doctor. Therefore, what you will find in this book is by no means presented as a 'miracle cure' for those with heart conditions. Rather, what I'm offering is a few ideas, backed up by helpful information, and is based on what I found helped me to get fit again after my heart attack. Any programme of exercise or particularly adventurous travel plans should always be thoroughly checked out with your GP or heart specialist first.

Chapter 2

Choosing Your First Trip

Working out what would suit you

Nothing makes me angrier than those smug articles in the colour supplements that assume that we all have high-pressure, well paid, 'important' jobs, and thus the cash to chill out in luxury Caribbean resorts, eating lobster and caviar – at prices that would nearly pay for a plumber to fix your leaking tap.

Your starting point, therefore, must be a realistic assessment of your health, your likes and dislikes, and the state of your bank account. If you really have been a serial couch potato all your life, and dread the idea of communal living and working outdoors in the damp or the blazing heat, the ideal first trip might not be a working holiday.

If you are naturally reserved or ill-at-ease in groups of complete strangers, then a trekking holiday through the Himalayas with a bunch of unreconstructed hearties, or a learn-to-sail holiday on a small boat with barely room to swing a Manx cat, might be tricky. On the other hand, there is a strong argument that says that this is the beginning of the new you, and that you need to reassess all the things you used to hate and look at them in a more positive light.

Perhaps the ultimate travel challenge for those with heart conditions would be a trip into space with Sir Richard Branson. His company, Virgin Galactic, is offering, by 2009, a quick ride beyond Earth's atmosphere. The cost of experiencing four to five minutes of weightlessness will be about £100,000. However, for the time being, I suggest you restrict your travels to Planet Earth.

Working out what would suit you

Over the centuries travel has followed clearly identifiable trends. From the Grand Tour of the 1800s to the Costa Brava beached whale holidays of the 1950s and 1960s, Brits tend to act like lemmings when we go on our travels. Many of us also like to take the UK way of life with us when we go in search of the sun and, despite the fact that we are obsessive travellers, a surprising number subscribe to the view of Uncle Matthew in Nancy Mitford's *The Pursuit of Love* that 'abroad is unutterably bloody and all foreigners are fiends'.

In the 1960s, many of my contemporaries took to the 'hippy trail', which involved hitching through Italy and the former Yugoslavia, romping through Iran and ending up somewhere in India or Nepal, where they lived out a blissful few months as high as the mountains around them. Others lounged in the sun or picked grapes in the South of France.

However, since those days a new trend for adventure and conservation holidays has emerged, with many of them targeted at older travellers. These active holidays are usually more heart-friendly than the layabout life of old.

Backpacking is no longer considered the preserve of the under-30s, although you do encounter young people by the thousand, weaving their way through Hong Kong, Bali, Cairns, the Great Barrier Reef, Sydney, Auckland and Fiji, with either a generous parental subsidy, or an extra student loan which will only have to be paid back in the unimaginably distant future. But older adventurers have unquestionably reclaimed some of this territory as their own.

The first rule of travel planning is to be thoroughly open-minded. You may 'know what you like and like what you know', but the familiar is not necessarily the best guide to what you are going to enjoy in the future.

For the computer literate, surfing the web is the best starting point for journey planning. I admit that in the early days of recovery from a heart condition, the last thing on your mind will be thoughts of adventure, whether at home or overseas. It is hard to think about the future when you are struggling to come to terms with the present. However on the 'get-back-on-your-bike-when-you-have-fallen-off' principle, I strongly recommend that you fire up your computer or visit your local travel agent as soon as you can. Then start some modest dreaming and planning.

Getting going

To start, take a look at the **British Heart Foundation** (BHF) website (*www.bhf.org.uk*; or ring its helpline tel: 08450 70 80 70), which contains some useful information about organisations that may be able to help on your first trip.

For the purposes of this book, I have assumed that your heart condition is sufficiently under control for you to travel without major assistance, and that you have a reasonable degree of physical strength and mobility. Nonetheless, in order to build up confidence, it may be a good idea for those who have had major heart surgery, for example, to consider taking their first trip with the help of an organisation that specifically helps those with disabilities.

Tourism for all (*www.tourismforall.org.uk*) (formerly **Holiday Care**), information line Tel: 0845 124 9971, is a registered charity that aims to help disabled and older people to lead independent lives by enhancing their ability to travel.

Although it does not arrange holidays or provide funding for them, it has a database of organisations that do so and provides information about transport, accommodation, visitor attractions and respite care establishments in the UK and overseas that can accommodate people with all kinds of disability.

However, if you feel confident enough to make the first travel move on your own, then I suggest you start by writing down everything you have always fancied doing, or have already enjoyed in the past. If your ideal holiday is to lie on a beach in the boiling sun, then I'm going to be a spoilsport. Assuming that you have spent some time in hospital and then several weeks recuperating, the last thing you need is more lounging time.

OK – we'll compromise. I'll allow you some chill-out time in the sunshine, but only if you combine it with some reasonably vigorous activity. There is good reasoning behind this. Exercise strengthens your heart muscle. It can also help you feel more energetic, put you more in control of your health and enable you to lose weight and keep it off. Exercise may also lower your blood pressure and reduce your cholesterol level.

A wealth of choices

A recent survey, carried out for the *Adventure and Travel Show*, indicated that there would be a steep increase in demand for adventure-based 'career breaks' for men and women in the next few years. (Of course, they would say that anyway, but it has the ring of truth.)

Whereas, with a few exceptions, adventure travel used to be a male prerogative, the number of women abandoning beach breaks for adventure holidays has doubled in ten years. They have even earned an acronym: INCA – Independent, No Children, Adventurous – although many female travellers I know go travelling in order to get a respite from their dependants. While 60% of women who go on adventure holidays are between 20 and 35, 20% are over 50.

While I am not suggesting that you necessarily should go on an extreme adventure holiday where you might put your health at risk – and anyway you should always consult your doctor before setting off – I do recommend that your trips involve a reasonable amount of exercise that involves your whole body, such as walking, cycling, jogging, cross-country skiing or swimming.

Therefore a skiing, walking or cycling holiday might be a good start, with sufficient time allowed for lazing around. (However, see elsewhere in this chapter about the dangers of very cold weather.) There are several travel companies that specialise in these activities and that grade holidays in order of the physical stamina required.

Some cater for special interests such as golf, bird watching, swimming, etc. Many are small one-man bands, while others are substantial travel companies. However their prices vary widely and it is best to set a budget and then see what you can get for your money.

If money is not too big an obstacle, a good starting point might be a company called **Inntravel** (*www.inntravel.co.uk*), which regularly wins awards for being the best UK travel company. Based in North Yorkshire, it offers independent walking and cycling holidays (among many others). Its holidays allow you explore what they claim to be some of Europe's finest footpaths. You walk at your own pace, not in a group, using detailed notes and maps to guide you. The company arranges for all your luggage to be transported ahead of you, so your heart is not put under undue strain by carrying a hefty rucksack or suitcase.

It also offers cycling holidays, which work on the same principle. You are given an itinerary and a map, and your luggage goes ahead of you. The company says that the emphasis throughout its programme is on relaxed discovery – what they call 'pootling' – and that the majority of its cycling holidays are accessible to all occasional cyclists.

When I called **Inntravel** to ask about the suitability of its holidays for people with a heart condition, the salesperson seemed somewhat surprised and had no advice to offer. However it does grade its walks from 1-to-3 and it would seem that Grade 1 ('easy, low-level walking with few ascents/descents but can have occasional long days') or Grade 2 ('moderate walking, on good surfaces, some long days and ascents/descents up to around 500m') would probably be okay if you are well on the road to recovery.

Another reputable company is **Explore Worldwide Ltd** (*www.explore.co.uk*), which offers a similar range of adventure holidays, but is perhaps a bit heartier and less 'posh'. However you need to be selective, as some of its holidays – particularly those to Peru – are quite tough going and involve some very high altitudes.

Explore Worldwide was founded in 1981 by three travelling companions who claim to have breathed, eaten and slept travel for as long as they can remember. Its original trips involved trekking across Iraq overland, Lima to Rio, the Nile by felucca (a traditional wooden sailing boat), and other slightly off-the-wall trips. Now it has 120 staff based in Farnborough, and offers 300 trips to over 100 countries, although Iraq is obviously no longer on the agenda.

It has a range of cycling and walking holidays, graded from 'easy' to 'strenuous'. For example it offers an 'easygoing' centre-based ramble in the Bulgarian hills, a moderate trek along the famous Camino de Santiago, and an adventurous trip combining a climb up Kilimanjaro with a safari in Tanzania. This may be too taxing for some, but the company does throw in a chill-out period on the beaches of Zanzibar.

Headwater (*www.headwater.com*) is another company that gets lots of plaudits from travellers. It offers guided and independent winter sports, walking and cycling holidays, mostly in Europe, as well as some in the Eastern Mediterranean, North Africa, Latin America and the Caribbean.

It operates activity holidays, which can be set up for you individually, or you can join a small group. If you go independently, you usually meet other travellers in especially chosen hotels each evening, which is a good compromise between independence and companionship. It has a one boot/two/three boots (or cycles) rating system, which should help you to ensure the right ratio of effort to enjoyment.

If your ambitions and purse are more modest, you will find a list of UK-based organisers of walking tours at the back of the book. For example, **Byways Breaks** (*www.byways-breaks.co.uk*) offers a three-day, three-night walking holiday along a 35 mile trail stretching from Disley to Kidsgrove, with some long climbs, steep but short ascents, ridge walks and views over the Cheshire plain. The first part of the walk is through Lyme Park, and then the trail climbs up onto the moors, through Macclesfield Forest and along the Dane valley. Then it follows Congleton Edge and finishes in Kidsgrove. There are stations at each end of the trail. You stay in pub/farmhouse B&Bs.

If this all sounds a bit too energetic, particularly if you are still recuperating, there are some equally interesting alternatives.

The next best thing to energetic physical exercise is mental stimulation. Taking well organised and not too physically demanding journeys to unusual places might be the solution if you are really not up to strenuous physical challenges. In Chapter 9, you will find my tale of a trip to the Arctic. There are a number of similar trips on small especially equipped ships to unusual parts of the world available. They do tend to be pricey, though, and if you are prone to seasickness, or are not too steady on your feet, they might not be the greatest choice. They usually involve getting in and out of dinghies and doing a certain amount of walking, but nothing that should faze the reasonably mobile.

One of the more reliable travel operators in this area is **Peregrine Adventures** (*www.peregrinadventures.co.uk*). This firm offers a wide range of marine adventure holidays, which are not too demanding physically but offer some great experiences. Each ship carries a medical officer which is quite reassuring, bearing in mind that you may be a very long way from a hospital These trips really come into their own if you are into marine biology or are a 'twitcher', wildlife enthusiast or botanist, and the tour guides are usually very knowledgeable.

Swim for your life

Swimming is very good exercise for the heart, but the problem is that many people find it pretty boring and, frankly, many of us aren't terribly good at it.

My nine year-old granddaughter is a much better swimmer than I am, and it sometimes occurs to me that if I was as accomplished as her, I might be tempted to spend more time at the local swimming baths.

Perhaps the answer is to combine travel and improving your swimming technique (or indeed learning to swim) by going on a specialised course.

There are a number of companies that organise such courses. One of the best ways of learning to swim or improving your skills is to take an intensive course such as those run weekly by **Swim Inn** (*www.hotel-northwales.com* or Tel: 01352 780503). The courses are run in conjunction with **The Springfield Hotel**, in Pentre Halkyn, Hollywell, overlooking the Dee estuary. For a price of £470 single or £435 shared, you get five days of intensive swimming coaching as well as full board in this comfortable hotel on the Welsh borders. You are even offered a money-back guarantee (not for the accommodation though). The course is in a 93°F heated indoor pool and every day you will have two,one hour pool sessions. The organisers promise small groups of people with the same fears as yourself (usually no more than four), the instructor in the pool, no spectators or other swimmers and individual tuition.

SwimTrek (*www.swimtrek.com*) claims to be the world's only swimming holiday operator to offer open water swimming tours in the Virgin Islands, Australia, Croatia, Greece, New Zealand, Malta and the UK. Participants go island- or lake-hopping, following routes of cultural, historical and geographical significance. The holidays are suitable for most standards of swimmer and the total weekly distance averages out at three miles a day. Time to rest and relax is built into each day of the holiday – it is not a swimming marathon. Island-hopping holidays work like sailing flotillas – you swim from island to island in groups, accompanied by a motorised escort.

The price includes a fully guided tour with safety escort, swim guiding, technique analysis, baggage handling, accommodation, breakfast and lunch. You have to pay for travel to and from the start of the tour and your evening meal.

Full swing and piste off

Golf and skiing are two of the more popular activity sports among the British. Golf in particular is an excellent form of gentle exercise for those with heart conditions. However, after a lot of thought, I decided not to include in this book many of the myriad golfing and skiing holidays on the market because information is readily available, and most golf and ski enthusiasts already know their favourite spots and tend to stick to them.

Although I have never played golf in my life, I do know that it is a more energetic activity than you might realise. It involves a lot of walking in the open air, as well as carrying clubs or pulling a trolley. As such it's good for stamina and strengthening the leg muscles.

Fortunately for those without a deep pocket (i.e. nearly all of us), most parts of the country have public golf courses where you can hire equipment if you want to try your hand at the game – probably a wise move before investing in a golfing holiday.

There are, of course, many private golf clubs, but they can be expensive to join and often have waiting lists. They also like to see themselves as 'exclusive', whatever that means. All you need is some basic equipment, including a set of clubs, comfortable outdoor shoes (or preferably special golf shoes) and an umbrella or rain gear.

Longshot Holidays (*www.longshotgolf.co.uk*) has been around for over thirty years, selling golfing holidays to destinations around the world from their offices in South Shields.

The company offers some very useful advice about choosing and surviving a golfing holiday, and rather than try to pick a selection of tour operators or recommended golf courses, I thought it more useful to reproduce (with its permission of course), its guide to surviving an overseas golf holiday without ruining it for yourself. Armed with this advice, you should find yourself on fairly safe ground.

Don't overdo it early on

A 3-to-4 hour flight, a night on the town and a strange bed is not the best preparation for the game of your life. You don't want to pull a muscle on the first day and be *hors de combat* for the rest of the week. So play yourself into the first day nice and easy. Leave the driver in the bag for a few holes, take out your trusty 3 or 5 wood and swing nice and slow. When you've played a few holes and loosened up a little, you can take out the big gun.

Don't handicap yourself by having no certificate

Many overseas clubs insist on handicap certificates. Many UK golfers do not have one. Spot the problem? If you haven't got a certificate, you need to put that right before you leave or you may struggle to get a game. If there isn't time to get a certificate, then get a written confirmation from your local pro or club secretary, stating that your playing ability is between 0 and 24. That will be accepted by many golf courses.

Solo is a no-no

One-balls have no standing. You can make your own jokes up there if you like, but its part of the etiquette of golf. It means that if you are playing on your own you are deemed to be practising on the course and you MUST let groups behind you through without delay. On a busy course you could end up standing on the side of the fairway, acting as a traffic policeman and calling everyone through. Not a lot of fun.

If you must play on your own, try to avoid playing before noon and choose a quiet course. Otherwise you could end up in the Guinness Book of Records for the longest round ever played. A good idea is to stay at a golf resort, where you can arrange to pair up with other guests. But your best bet is to enter one of the many overseas golf tournaments. This will ensure you get a partner and a problem-free round.

Early birds catch more than worms

If you don't mind playing before 0800 and after 1200, you can book your tee times when you like. But a four ball of George Bush, Gordon Brown, Nicolas Sarkozy and Vladimir Putin would struggle to get a 0900 tee time if they left their booking till three months before the day. And if they did succeed, the course probably wouldn't be worth playing on. If you really want to choose the time you play, book at least four months in advance or you could be disappointed.

Swinging in the rain

Keeping the courses in perfect condition is no mean feat and is not helped by Mother Nature at her worst. Whilst the hotels and clubs do their best to keep the course in tip-top shape, holiday companies will not take responsiblity for the playing conditions or state of the courses.

Local Levies

Some local golf clubs charge a small fee for golf insurance and local taxes, so to ensure a stress free tee off, pay before you play.

Skiing is more physically demanding than golf, and you must take medical advice before setting off for the snow. Extreme cold weather may affect your heart: your heart rate and blood pressure may go up and your blood vessels may constrict. In fact, the number of people admitted to hospital with heart attacks tends to increase during winter months, and cold temperatures can act as a trigger for angina attacks.

Very cold weather can cause changes to the blood, activating blood platelets which can increase your risk of developing blood clots. Therefore, those with heart conditions should wrap up warmly or stay indoors when things get really chilly.

Recycle

Cycling is an excellent aid to fitness, providing you don't become one of those maniacs who seem intent on mowing down any pedestrian that has the temerity to walk along a pavement, footpath or towpath. I have encountered almost as many *kamakaze* cyclists as I have motorists, although I admit they are more of an annoyance than a threat to life.

Cyclists tend to be somewhat smug in their tight-fitting shorts and rather uncool safety helmets, and their tendency to jump lights, shout at pedestrians and motorists, and pedal hell-for-leather towards the nearest animate object, does not exactly endear them to me.

Having had my grumble, there is no question that gentle cycling holidays are ideal for those with mild heart conditions. Cycling regularly will improve your fitness and can help you live a long and healthy life. Providing cyclists behave with consideration for pedestrians, cycling is also good news for the environment and your local community but, most importantly, your strength, stamina, aerobic fitness and general muscle function will all be improved.

Cycling is a low impact activity and one of the safest ways to exercise without risk of over-exertion or strain to muscles and joints. Regular physical activity also facilitates other healthy behaviour and could help you reduce weight or even give up smoking.

For those with heart problems, the benefit of cycling is that it helps to strengthen heart muscles, resting pulse is lowered and blood fat levels reduced. Furthermore, by burning body fat and raising your metabolic rate, you can lose weight. Cycling is one of the more comfortable forms of physical activity for those who are new to exercise, allowing most people to get fit easily and safely without undue physical strain.

You will find a list of useful cycling websites and contacts in Part 3, but a good starting point is to contact the **Cyclists' Tourist Club** (*www.ctc.org*), the grandaddy of cycling organisations. Helpline Tel: 0870 873 0060.

CTC is the UK and Ireland's largest and longest established national cycling membership organisation. It was founded in 1878 as the Bicycle Touring Club, subsequently becoming the Cyclists' Touring Club. In 2003 it celebrated 125 years of working for travelling, recreational and utility cycle users.

CTC has over 700 information sheets describing routes all over the world, but it also has a good number of information sheets which cover more general topics. For example it tells you how to bag up your bike if you want to fly off with it and highlights the problems associated with taking your bike on trains in this country.

Going Wild

One of the more unusual ways of getting out and about is to go on a Bushcraft course. For a modest fee, you can set off for North Yorkshire where an outfit called **Taste The Wild** (*www.tastethewild.co.uk*) will spend a weekend teaching you the basics of bushcraft living. You will be introduced to the tools and skills needed to work in green wood (unseasoned logs to you and me). No power tools here, just instruments of torture such as the drawknife, side axe and shave horse, along with the shaping and joining techniques of green wood building. Over the weekend, you will help to create a greenwood structure from materials found in the woods. The cost of the course includes use of tools, camping in a tepee in the woods and food cooked for you on open fires.

Bushcraft has become quite a cult recently and there is even an annual festival called the **Wilderness Gathering**. **Taste The Wild** also runs wild foods weekend at the same price, where you learn to identify and forage for seasonal edible plants and fruits and learn about their preparation. However this is not for the squeamish. You also learn about the preparation and cooking of wild game birds and animals, along with more exotic dishes of insects and grubs – using, naturally, ecologically friendly simple pots and tools to cook over an open fire.

If you want to go further afield and fancy living in a cave for a couple of days, **Islay Bushcraft** (*www.islaybushcraft.co.uk*) offers you the opportunity to taste life on the 'outer edge' as they put it. Islay – an island in the Hebrides – is better known for its whisky than its cave dwellers but the owner, Jeremy Hastings, promises that you will leave no trace of your visit. The only rubbish you'll leave behind is junk mail, predictive texting, multiple TV channels, to-do lists, remote controls, supermarket queues, one-way systems and traffic jams.

He calls himself an 'independent educator/facilitator and ranger guide' and has spent thirty years travelling and teaching, exploring and experiencing nature at its wildest.

Hobby Horses

One way of getting exercise is to join an organisation that caters specifically for one of your personal interests and organises specialist walks or holidays.

For example, I have a layman's interest in twentieth-century architecture and have joined the **Twentieth Century Society** (*www.c20society.org.uk*) which organises fascinating day-long walks and longer trips to places in the UK and overseas, where there is a lot of interesting modern architecture.

It costs around £30 a year to join the society which fights for the preservation of post-1914 architecture that is neglected by the better known Victorian Society, founded by John Betjeman and Nikolaus Pevsner.

It promotes a variety of activities which are only open to members – though to be a member you simply have to express an interest and pay your sub.

In summer, walks and other visits are organised to see buildings in all parts of the British Isles. The tours may last just one day, or span a weekend. The leaders are always highly knowledgeable and seem to be able to open the doors to otherwise secret interiors and gain entry to long-forgotten buildings.

Excellent detailed notes accompany each visit and you get the chance of guided visits to places like Dublin, Nice, Antwerp, Berlin, Brussels, Chicago, Dublin, Helsinki, Ljubljana, Milan, Prague and New York. However, these tours are very popular, and you have to be quick off the mark to get a place on some of them.

Even the day trips usually involve three or four hours of solid walking, although much of it is along pavements and roads. I have explored the back streets of Brixton, the parks of Docklands and the amazing houseboats and bungalows of Shoreham-by-Sea.

At risk of digressing, I recommend a visit to Shoreham-by-Sea, even if you are not interested in architecture. The town, which is just up the road from Brighton, used to have an area called Bungalow Town, which as it name implies, was full of bungalows. These were made from old railway carriages, set about fifteen feet apart with a concrete raft in between them, covered by a corrugated iron roof. The railway carriages were bedrooms and the living area was the space in between.

These bungalows were much favoured by musical hall stars and actors such as Marie Luftus, Lupino Lane and 'Monsewer' Eddie Gray who regularly performed down the road in Brighton. The result of this critical mass of stars was that one of the earliest film studios in the UK was set up here in the early 1900s by a scenic artist named Francis Lyndhurst, a relative of Nicholas Lyndhurst (Rodney from *Only Fools And Horses*). Apparently he chose the location of Shoreham because it had pure, smog-free air and the quality of light was clearer.

Sadly no signs of the film studio are left apart from a fading plaque on a nearby church, and only a few of the bungalows survived because most were flattened at the orders of the wartime government in case they provided shelter to invading Germans. But somehow our leaders from the **Twentieth Century Society** got us acccess visits to those that have survived, and they were absolutely fascinating.

After the war, a motley assortment of houseboats sprang up and many are still there, including a former German minesweeper and a boat that appears to be built partly from two old buses welded together. We had an intriguing poke around several of these houseboats and found a vaguely arty community who were keen to show us their nautical works of art. They also complained bitterly about the local council which would prefer to have another soulless marina full of posh boats that would rarely be used, but whose owners would pay lots of lovely rates to fill up the municipal coffers.

There are hundreds of similar organisations offering trips that involve a fair amount of exercise and travel, but it would be impossible to list them all here. However the best starting point is a web site called ***www.travel-quest.co.uk*** which has links to a vast number of companies and associations that organise trips for those with special interests.

I suggest that you think about your particular interests and hobbies – or, better still, things that you are vaguely interested in but have never pursued in the past – and then click on this website. Alternatively, just do a Google search or visit your local library (if one still exists in your area).

Among the special activities I found, by hunting around on this site and in the local library, were adventure sports, ball and racquet games, cycling, riding, fishing, shooting, mountaineering, motor sports, running, caving, watersports, winter sports, arts and crafts, dance, gardening, health and fitness, history and archaeology, technology and wildlife.

Dreaming in the rain

Some people dream of re-enacting something they have read in a book or seen on television or in the cinema. There is no reason why you shouldn't turn this fantasy into reality in the form of an activity holiday.

A book I enjoyed reading in my teens was Jerome K Jerome's *Three Men in a Boat,* which tells the story of the author's trip up the Thames with his two friends, George and Harris. Written in 1889, the book charts the mishaps and meanderings of the hopeless trio and their dog Montmorency as they blunder along the river in a small rowing boat.

It's possible – indeed almost fashionable – to re-create this trip, helped by **Thames Skiff Holidays** (*www.skiffhire.com*) which hires out traditional camping skiffs from its base in Walton-on-Thames. Prices include camping equipment and are based on a round trip. One-way rentals are possible and boats can be delivered or picked up from any slipway on the Thames for an additional charge.

Phil Turner and his two brothers Pete and Bob, decided that this would be the ideal trip to create a bit of brotherly bonding and to get some exercise. Phil will not see 70 again and had the misfortune to crash a glider plane a few years ago when the towrope snapped, leaving him with several creaking joints and the odd missing internal organ.

Nonetheless the three recently set off in pouring rain, arguing over who was Jerome, who was George and who was Harris (see p. 28).

Volunteering

One of the most notable changes in people's attitudes to holidays and foreign travel has been a sudden upsurge of interest in actually getting involved in the lives of overseas countries, rather than just flopping on a beach and being waited on by the long-suffering locals.

The tourism industry expects the biggest rise in demand in the next few years to be in 'responsible tourism'. Industry experts claim that the biggest growth will be among tour companies that specialise in voluntary conservation and charity work, especially holidays that tap into an increasingly widespread desire 'to do something useful', in

It was all the fault of my younger brother Pete. We bought him a first edition of one of his favourite books, *Three Men in a Boat,* for his sixtieth birthday and it reminded him of the enormous fun that he and his little brother Bob had on, in, and around the river nearly 50 years ago.

Within a week he phoned me to suggest that the three of us get together and, using the book as a model, have a week on the Thames. He had already propositioned Bob, searched the web, and found a small company that hired out Victorian camping skiffs.

I hesitated for about a millisecond before agreeing. It has always been my ambition to grow old disgracefully and this seemed like a significant step in the right direction. As the plan was elaborated we decided that we would follow as directly as possible in the footsteps of Jerome K Jerome's heroes. We would start from as near Kingston as we could. We would take a small tent for one of us and the other two would sleep under the canvas awning of the boat. If the weather was foul we might take refuge in a pub for the night. We would also exactly retrace their path by rowing upstream to Oxford, 91 miles and 31 locks. Circumstances even ensured that we did it at the same time of the year, the third week in May.

Just after three o' clock on a spring Wednesday, the three of us shoved off from the landing slip at Thames Ditton. Pete and Bob were at the sculls and I was on the rudder lines. I uttered a confident and seamanlike cry of 'give way!' and we rowed out manfully into the stream. At this point Judy, our chauffeuse, began to look less apprehensive, but we rather spoiled it by hailing her to ask which way was upstream.

Once this tricky point was resolved, we made our farewells and set off pulling along the boundary of Hampton Court palace.

It was bright when we started out but the sky had been clouding over for a while and it was not long before it started to rain. At this point we were very pleased that our gear was all stowed in waterproof stuff bags. Three hours later, it was still drizzling and we made our first night's camp moored alongside a rather muddy island near Shepperton. It was something of a pantomime.

None of us had erected a camping cover since I was a lad, the Victorian folding hoops seemed intent on inflicting painful injuries on our fingers, and the heavy canvas cover weighed more than we remembered. Eventually we got it up, Bob's tent was pitched, and with the aid of an entrenching tool, sanitary facilities were provided in an adjacent thicket. This first night, it took well over an hour and a half to set up camp but we got faster with practice.

Once order was established, Pete cooked supper and I opened the first bottle of wine. We washed up in the river and then opened the second bottle. We followed that with Pete's secret camping potion, hot chocolate laced with about a quadruple brandy and by bedtime we were three deeply contented men. When we retired to our sleeping bags, we slept like logs. We woke at about seven the next morning, breakfasted on tea, dried fruit and muesli, struck the tent and the cover, tidied the camp site and rowed off up river.

That first day set the pattern except that we abandoned the notion of cooking a main meal in the evenings as the weather worsened. From then on we found a pub for a couple of pints, a substantial lunch and coped with plenty of tea and cold food for breakfast and supper, besides making serious inroads on the European wine and brandy lake.

The weather worsened and the wind was pretty consistently against us. On one day, it recorded a mean speed of 25 knots, and as the heavy rain continued, the lock keepers progressively opened the weir sluices and the current ran faster and faster. Passing through Reading, we were overtaken by a three year-old riding a fairy-cycle along the towpath and several times we were rowing flat out and only just managed to breast the current, while we hunted across the stream for slack water.

On the fourth night we decided that a shower and a dry bed would be a good idea but discovered that most of the cheerful riverside pubs of our youth had been tarted up and become hideously expensive. What is more, in our wet and mud splattered condition, we would have been about as welcome as a mild dose of amoebic dysentery.

In the end, the friendly keeper at Sonning lock introduced us to 'J' and Charlotte, the owners of the hotel boat *Actief* which was moored just above the lock. Despite the fact that they had just said farewell to a full complement of guests, and had been looking forward to an evening off, they provided comfortable beds, hot showers, a great deal of wine and a magnificent breakfast.

Restored by good company and this touch of luxury, we pressed on upstream and despite being awarded a yellow card, which told us that the current was now too strong for unpowered boats, we continued to head for Oxford and became increasingly confident that we were going to make it. We developed a sneaking feeling of superiority when we encountered two more of Tom Balm's skiffs coming downstream. The crew of one of them announced that they had asked to be retrieved after only two days.

Despite the weather, we were having a ball and despite an average age of sixty- two, reverting to our juvenile selves. We are not the sort of blokes to take readily to stuffed toys but Montmorency, the toy dog that had been loaned to us in place of Jerome's very real one, began to develop a personality.

Dafter still, we decided that we were on a quest and adopted the characters of Voltarol, Alcohol and Ganja the Dwarf.

Any one that has suffered from arthritis will be familiar with Voltarol, Alcohol needs no explanation, and two years teaching in a school for naughty boys provided me with the third name. We later added a fourth character to our pantheon, Offa's Dyke, a Celtic princess of indeterminate gender.

The week wasn't merely a combination of a nostalgia fest, an endurance trial and a geriatric booze cruise. It was also a journey through a positively magical landscape. Once above Windsor, apart from a rather dreary passage through Reading, the Thames Valley is every bit as beautiful as it was fifty years ago.

There wasn't very much river traffic and because a rowing boat makes very little noise, the wild life took next to no notice of us and we saw at close range red kites, parakeets, herons, innumerable water-fowl, and a quietly busy little water vole. The banks were as leafy as ever and the May blossom brought to mind hackneyed comparisons with lace and foam, and an odour that booted all three of us back to being about ten years old again.

The lock keepers were almost universally helpful, there were still a few cheerful unpretentious riverside pubs which gave us a very warm welcome and most of the folks we shared the river with were friendly and good natured.

When we emerged from the final lock at Iffley we ran directly into a flotilla of Oxford regatta crews who were evidently bewildered by a trio of elderly hooligans chanting 'Voltarol, Alcohol and Ganja the Dwarf' but before we could get in to serious trouble, we reached the slipway above Donnington Bridge, where two daughters and three grandchildren were cheering and waving flags at us.

Rosalind was hauled out of the River and on to Tom Balm's trailer, and our voyage was over. Despite a few creaks, aches and pains, none of us wants to wait for another 48 years before we do it again.

addition to the enjoyment of the adventure.

Inevitably, some of the travel companies that cash in on this interest will be more solid than others, so check them out carefully before parting with any money. It is worth noting that some small companies operate under someone else's ATOL licence (the Air Travel Organiser's License which is a requirement of the Civil Aviation Authority for all UK tour operators wishing to sell seats on chartered or scheduled flights). This necessitates a financial 'health check' and putting up a bond to cover the expense of reimbursing/ repatriating tourists in the event of operator failure. It is quite legal to operate under someone else's ATOL, but means that you may not know who is supposed to be protecting you if something goes wrong.

There is also anecdotal evidence that one or two of these companies are charging quite a bit of money without fully ensuring that the volunteer activity is properly organised. So be prepared to ask plenty of questions and make whatever inquiries you can to ensure that everything looks above board before you hand over any money.

One way of saving money is to approach the volunteer organisation that is making the on-the-ground arrangements and negotiate directly with them. Several companies selling volunteer holidays are, effectively, commission agents and have nothing to do with the actual work arrangements. I know for a fact that there is at least one volunteering organisation which charges half the cost you would pay through an agent, if you book directly through them.

However let's start by assuming that UK-based companies offer the best and simplest method of making your arrangements.

I have already mentioned that the **National Trust** (*www.nationaltrust.org.uk*) runs working holidays, which last either a week or weekend. You usually sleep in fairly basic but clean base camps with a leader who does the shopping, organises volunteers to help with the cooking and washing up and drives you to the work site. You will find more about my own experiences in Chapter 6, but in general the work involves clearing undergrowth, chopping down trees, building fences, stone walls, etc.

The **BTCV** (British Trust for Conservation Volunteers) (*www.btcv.org*) is another charity that arranges practical conservation work for volunteers throughout Britain. It supports many local groups across the country, runs training courses and organises working holidays. It is a great way to get experience of the conservation industry and many full-time workers started off volunteering for it.

It organises a wide variety of breaks of different lengths all over the country, as well as in mainland Europe and further afield. However, it tends to be much more expensive than the National Trust but has a greater choice of activities and destinations and much better availability.

I have done four spells with BTCV, including ten days in Scotland clearing out a pond and rebuilding the sides with clay walls, as well as stripping a quarter of a mile of ivy from an eighteenth century walled garden. On this occasion, most of the participants were far younger than me but it was good fun, if very hard work, as I spent most of my time in water up to my waist. The group was multi-national and I struck a good deal with one very strong French lad: he did all the hard work and I translated for him and taught him English. On other working holidays, I have stayed in accommodation ranging from a former vicarage to a scout hut with a distinct whiff of unwashed youth.

BTCV also organises local groups and 'Green Gyms' for older people who want to get a bit of regular exercise.

Another good starting point might be a company called **Real Gap Experience** (*www.gapyearforgrownups.co.uk*), based in Tunbridge Wells, which has also spawned a subsidiary called **Gap Year for Grown Ups**. This operation specialises in providing opportunities for people of all ages to take time out from work to travel and do volunteer work around the world. It also takes care of such practicalities as visas, insurance, and so on.

Among its offerings are the opportunity to spend four weeks with **Conservation Volunteers Australia** (*www.conservationvolunteers.com.au*) (again you can find out more in Chapter 12), working on a number of conservation projects, as well as projects in Botswana, Namibia, South Africa, Zimbabwe and Kenya.

Another possibility is to volunteer to work with children in Africa, helping poor communities to help themselves. You can work with grassroots organisations to bring some fun into the lives of children affected by Aids/HIV, taking them to the zoo or the beach, teaching them new skills and helping to brighten their surroundings.

You can also learn Spanish for four weeks in a language school, then work on volunteer projects and travel around a choice of Latin American countries including Argentina, Bolivia, Brazil, Costa Rica, Ecuador, Guatemala, Mexico and Peru. However do remember the risks of high altitudes, particularly in Bolivia, Ecuador and Peru. There are also volunteering opportunities in India and Thailand.

If you are a doctor, nurse or medical administrator you can volunteer for a three month stint abroad with **Médecins du Monde** (*www.medecinsdumonde.org.uk*) which sends medical volunteers such as surgeons, doctors, nurses, midwifes and psychologists on humanitarian missions. Volunteers must have at least two years' experience and be available for a minimum of three months.

Non-medical positions for administrators, logisticians and non-medical co-ordinators are also available to ensure that the projects run effectively. For all posts, international experience is desirable and some knowledge of French and/or Spanish is useful.

When **Médecins du Monde** sends people into the field, it covers the costs of transportation, food, housing and insurance (cover for medical expenses, life insurance, legal cover and repatriation on medical or security grounds). In addition, all staff receive an allowance of £105–£210 per month – depending on local circumstances – as soon as they arrive in the field. All staff also get a monthly sum of £400–£600 paid into their bank account at home.

It is somewhat shaming that this organisation has felt the need to launch *Project: London* to help improve access to health care for vulnerable groups in the capital. This is an advocacy project that provides information, advice and practical assistance to vulnerable people to help them access NHS and other services. In order to reach the most hard-to-reach groups, volunteer teams provide basic health care in the interim period, until these people reach mainstream services.

The granddaddy of volunteering is **Voluntary Service Overseas** (*www.vso.org.uk*), which has been in operation for nearly 50 years. In a sense what VSO offers is slightly outside the remit of this book, as it is looking for a commitment of at least a year and there is a modest level of remuneration. It is also not too happy to take on volunteers with health problems, but if you have the time to spare, and are qualified in those areas where there is greatest demand

– health and education, public and private sector management and IT
– then it may well be worth finding out more.

Another organisation that tries to bridge the gap between volunteering and adventure holidays is New Zealand-based **Hands Up Holidays** (*www.handsupholidays.com*), which aims to give travellers the opportunity not only to see interesting sights, but to have 'authentic interaction' (whatever that might mean) with local people and make a contribution to local communities.

According to the MD Christopher Hill, his firm is committed to providing its clients with 'authentic experiences with real people'. The idea is that part of your trip is based on a conventional adventure holiday, with a community development project sandwiched in the middle. A typical trip to Argentina will have the following itinerary. You first fly to the Iguaçu Falls with a 4WD-jungle excursion, then you move on to Bahia Blanca in Patagonia, where you take part in a four-day community development project.

Afterwards, you transfer to El Calafete to the Merino glacier where you go ice climbing. This is followed by a trip to Chile's Torres del Paine, then on by plane to Ushuaia, at the world's southernmost city, where you sail into the Beagle Channel before returning to Buenos Aires.

Travel for charity

There has been a growing interest in expeditions which raise money for charity and there are now specialised operators which organise and co-ordinate these events on behalf of a wide variety of charitable organisations.

An organisation called **Across the Divide Expeditions** (*www.acrossthedivide.com*) might be a good starting point. It organises its own general charity expeditions and organises others for specific charities.

It was set up to provide adventurous and safe fundraising activities such as treks, bike rides, community projects, dog sledding and white-water rafting as charity challenges. Its destinations range from the Great Wall of China and Torres de Paine National Park in Patagonia to local ventures in Wiltshire, Cheshire and Ireland. The company says that it ploughs back some of its profits into these fund raising efforts and that it has contributed £50,000 to projects in Africa.

The company's website offers a wide range of charities and destinations to choose from. You can either contact the charity itself via a link on the website or deal with **Across the Divide** after you have decided who you want to support or where you want to go.

You have to pledge to raise a minimum sponsorship and complete registration, medical and insurance forms and return them with a registration fee. Obviously you shouldn't volunteer to take part in an expedition which is beyond your physical capacity, and you should certainly discuss your heart condition with the company or the charity you have chosen. However the company provides professional expedition medics for all its own expeditions, and runs a special expedition medicine course to train doctors for this type of activity.

Squaring your employer

As I mentioned earlier, for those who are not retired, taking time off work when you have already been off sick, may be tricky. If your employer has a medical or occupation health department, it makes sense to speak to it first. Large international companies, in particular, should be able to give you useful information about health facilities in countries you may wish to visit.

Gap Year for Grown Ups offers some useful tips on negotiating with your employer:

- It is essential that you form a plan of action before speaking to your employer, and outlining the possible benefits to the company is just as important as explaining your personal reasons for taking time out.
- The first thing to do is to research the official/unofficial company policy on leaves of absence − if there isn't one this doesn't mean you can't go; prepare your case and speak to your boss regardless. The lack of formal policy may mean that this is a more flexible issue.

- Remember that whatever you choose to do on your sabbatical, be it teaching English to children in China, or trekking in Nepal, you will not only learn more about yourself but also develop valuable commercial skills in team building, tolerance and communication.
- Your achievements will be unique assets on your CV, giving you an edge on competitors.
- Taking a career break at the right time can prevent serious burn-out which might result in stress, disillusionment or even a nervous breakdown, particularly for those with heart problems.
- If you are having serious doubts about your chosen career, this break could give you the chance to try out a new vocation, or at the very least, rethink your options.
- If you are to be employed by the company throughout your trip, it is important to arrange a means not only of contacting the company but of staying involved. This may mean regular e-mails, or even subscribing to a company magazine that is sent out to your project.
- Make sure that you discuss your pension package, as you will need to organise a payments break with your employer. If you have been an employee for less than two years, you are entitled to a refund of your contributions and you can transfer your pension rights to a pension plan offered by another provider.

Protecting your travel arrangements

As with everything in life, you need to be a bit streetwise when booking a trip. For example, if you book through a travel company, make sure it has an ATOL licence, as mentioned earlier. Most firms who sell air travel in the UK are required by law to have one.

This licence protects you from losing money or being stranded abroad when a tour operator goes out of business. All licensed firms have to lodge bonds with the CAA. This is so that if they go out of business, the CAA can give refunds and arrange for those stranded abroad to finish their holidays and fly home. There's also a

Government-backed fund called the Air Travel Trust that steps in if any ATOL bond isn't big enough to look after everyone affected by a failure.

However you should remember that this only covers you if you buy a flight as part of the package. You are not covered if you purchase an air ticket directly from an airline, whether by phone, in person or via the internet, or indeed from an IATA travel agent, if the ticket is issued on the spot. In this event, your contract will be with the airline, which should honour your ticket even if the agent goes out of business. You should also note that an ATOL licence might not protect you if you aren't in the UK when you make your booking.

To make life even more complicated, a recent Appeal Court decision means that travel agents who sell package holidays can now split the holiday into separate flight and accommodation contracts, thereby avoiding the need to guarantee financial protection for travellers. Thus it now pays travel agents to unravel packages and sell the component parts separately – thereby avoiding the need to pay for an ATOL bond. In other words, booking a holiday is becoming increasingly risky – but then what isn't these days?

There is one reasonably foolproof safeguard however: buy your tickets with a credit (not debit) card. Then, if your airline or holiday company goes belly-up, you should get your money back from the credit card company. The downside is that you sometimes have to pay a surcharge of 2% for paying by credit card, but it seems like worthwhile protection. However don't expect a refund to be easy. You'll get your money, but be ready for a long fight.

Buying by credit card is also the only way to protect yourself against fraud. **The Association of British Travel Agents** (ABTA) used to refund travellers if they were victims of fraud by one of its members. It has now changed its rules and will no longer compensate victims, but will still shell out if your travel agent goes broke.

Be wary of using some of the well-known internet travel companies. While their websites are usually fairly easy to use, their terms and conditions are often obscure, and if you eventually manage to speak to someone, you are quite likely to be given the wrong information. I ended up buying a ticket I didn't really want from one internet company, which had lured me through a hard-sell TV advertising campaign. Of course the company wouldn't change or refund it, despite the implication on its website that it would.

On the whole, it is easier, and often as cheap, to buy tickets directly from airlines' own websites, and you are less likely to have problems as a result.

I reckon, however, that if you have a heart problem, in order to keep your stress levels down, it would be better to go to a good travel agent or use one of the reputable flight specialists like **Trailfinders** (*www.trailfinders.com*), who have pretty good customer service and whose agents know what they are talking about.

Chapter 3

Getting Ready

Health Tips, Insurance, Drug Management, etc.

I don't wish to be the bearer of bad news, but in a book of this nature it seems irresponsible not to set all the facts before you. I would certainly like to drink to your health, but not before we've all taken a sober look at the pros and cons of travelling with a heart condition.

As I have emphasised, I am no medical expert, so most of the information in this chapter comes from the literature and websites of a variety of bodies and individuals. I have acknowledged my sources wherever possible. You should also check out for yourself anything you are unsure about, as this book doesn't come with any medical guarantees. However, the aim of this chapter is to save you days of scouring web sites and calling medical experts for advice.

When is it safe to travel?

The first and most important step for all heart patients who plan to travel is to have a complete physical exam and get an accurate assessment of your current physical health. The biggest risk a heart patient can take is to go on a trip unprepared. I managed to get an angiogram (a catheter-based test that provides detailed images of your heart and blood vessels) done privately before I went to Australia, but it can take several months to get one done on the NHS.

Although it is much harder to get non-urgent tests done in the UK than the USA, unless you have private medical insurance, it is advisable to test your heart capacity well in advance of a planned trip. Treadmill stress tests, thallium scans or programmed ventricular stimulation can all help to predict how much altitude and activity you can tolerate.

If you really want to be safe, it may be wise to have a homocysteine blood test. High homocysteine levels in the blood can cause cholesterol to change to something called oxidized low-density lipoprotein, which damages the arteries. In addition, high homocysteine levels may make blood clot more easily than it should. This can increase the risk of blood vessel blockages.

You might also consider the Rolls Royce of tests – an Electron Beam Tomography (EBT) scan. This is now one of the major screening devices for the detection of coronary artery disease. Ten times faster than more traditional CT scans, EBT is considered ideal for detection of calcification in coronary arteries. In effect, the screening allows doctors to act promptly and initiate preventive techniques that might not ordinarily be considered in early stages of illnesses.

A third 'state of the art' test is a Heart Rate Variability test. Some of these tests may not be available on the NHS, so they may only be available if you have private medical insurance or a deep pocket.

Most people with stable heart disease that is monitored and controlled should have no problem travelling. However the **American Heart Association**, for example, advises that if you have had open-heart surgery, you are best advised to avoid air travel for six weeks and to keep clear of high altitudes for six months because blood vessels that have been operated on may re-narrow 6–12 weeks after surgery. If you have had a heart attack within the past four weeks, air travel is definitely not recommended.

Also, expanding gases could cause great discomfort, and airsickness with vomiting could put excessive strain on healing tissues. The AHA stresses that a heart patient really should not be far from home until sure that he or she is stable. Unstable angina, congestive heart failure (CHF) and abnormal heart rhythm are all good reasons for staying close to home.

Different types of heart disease require different precautions. For example, people with CHF should avoid high-altitude destinations, while people with valvular heart problems may experience changes in their prothrombin (clotting) time when taking malaria pills.

There's a growing body of evidence to suggest that heart attacks are closely linked with extremes in weather conditions, especially when it is very cold.

Several studies have reported a link between extremes in temperature and deaths from coronary heart disease and strokes. This is especially apparent among the elderly. In countries that have very hot summer weather, hospital admission rates tend to increase when temperatures rise. If you have coronary heart disease, extreme heat may place an extra burden on the heart and circulation. This is because the body's natural cooling mechanism can't work as effectively in humid conditions as it can in a drier climate.

Therefore, if you have any sort of heart disease, it is best to avoid sitting in the sun, especially between 1100 and 1500. You should stay in the shade as much as possible, and drink plenty of fluids. It is also important to avoid drinking excessive alcohol during the daytime, as you will risk getting dehydrated. If you can't resist a drink, swallow a glass of water for every glass of alchohol, or dilute wine with soda (a spritzer). If you go for a walk, pace yourself – and if possible, walk with a friend. Take a hat, sun cream, something to drink and choose a well-shaded path.

If you are flying, you may need to contact the medical department of your airline before setting off. This will allow airline medical staff to assist with early boarding or a wheelchair if needed, and to provide appropriate in-flight care. Airlines can be quite fussy about health issues and when I asked for an aisle seat on a Japan Airlines flight to Tokyo, explaining I needed to be able to walk around to prevent DVT, it provoked a flurry of demands for letters from my cardiologist and GP, confirming that I was fit to fly.

However the result was two seats to myself on each flight, with extra legroom and very attentive service, so it was worth all the fuss.

Of course I was under no obligation to say I had had a heart attack when booking the flight, but it does illustrate the panic that the words 'heart problems' can induce in travel operators and insurance companies.

If you have implantable cardioverter defibrillators (ICDs) or a pacemaker, you may need to have a certificate of fitness to travel. The metal in your pacemaker can trigger the alarm in some airport security systems, although this happens rarely. If you have concerns about passing through airport security systems, it would be wise to discuss this with your doctor before you travel. It is always best to explain at security that you have a pacemaker or an ICD fitted. You can usually bypass the system and security staff may carry out a manual body search – now very common anyway. In some airports, staff may use a hand-held scanner to do a manual search. The scanner may come close to your pacemaker or ICD but there are rarely problems with this.

Generally, if you walk straight through the frame without lingering, there should be no effect. However, if you have either a pacemaker or ICD, you are advised to avoid standing in walk-through metal detectors for more than 15 seconds. Hand-held metal detectors are also safe for people with defibrillators, but prolonged contact, such as holding the detector over the defibrillator for more than five seconds, should be avoided.

It may also be a good idea to contact the **St George's ICD Support Group** (Tel: 020 8725 1372), which can supply more information about travel for patients with ICDs.

The British Thoracic Society Air Travel Working Party (*www.brit-thoracic.org.uk*) also recommends that people should avoid flying within six weeks of major surgery and should have heparin injections if they need to travel during that period. It also suggests you should ask your doctor whether you may need aspirin pre-flight and compression stockings.

For independent information, reference and comment on aviation health issues such as deep vein thrombosis (DVT), cardiovascular and pulmonary risks, it is worth contacting **The Aviation Health Institute** (*www.aviation-health.org*), which promotes the health and well-being of airline passengers world-wide (see listings at the end of the book for details).

Basic travel health rules
You should always keep with you:

*   A list of all drugs you are taking. Use generic names, and indicate dosages, as drug formulations vary from country to country.
*   A copy of a baseline electrocardiogram.
*   The name and contact information of your doctor.
*   A brief letter from your doctor (on letterhead paper, signed

and dated) that describes your condition, the need for any supplies or medications, and information on any implanted pacemakers or cardiac defibrillators you may have.

- More than enough of each of your medications to cover the length of your trip, as medication may be difficult to refill once you reach your destination.

Here are some other basic rules:

- Check with your doctor or pharmacist to be sure that any medications prescribed specifically for your trip (e.g. malaria pills) do not interfere with your heart medications. All medications should be kept in their original containers.
- Put all your medical information and medications in your carry-on bag to avoid losing them in lost luggage.
- Stay hydrated: be sure to drink plenty of water during your flight to ensure hydration in the dehydrating plane atmosphere. Avoid excess alcohol, tea and coffee.
- Try to eat well in advance of a night flight (unless you are flying first or business class, the airline meal is likely to be quite resistable anyway), and have food with a low-glycaemic index such as fruit, pulses, bran cereals etc.
- Always try to get an aisle seat so that you can easily stretch and move around the cabin at least once every hour. If it is difficult to walk in the aisle, you should move your feet – raising your toes with your heels on the ground – for several minutes every half-hour.
- Support stockings may be beneficial on long-haul flights. According to research published recently by the **Cochrane Library** (an international medical resource base, which is partially funded by the NHS), wearing compression stockings when flying results in a very large reduction in symptomless DVT. Passengers who wear stockings also suffer far less discomfort and swelling in their legs (oedema) than those who do not wear them. Its research showed that wearing stockings reduces the risk of DVT from around 30 in every 1,000 passengers to two or three in every 1,000. In other words, it's worth wearing

the stockings even if they are a bit uncomfortable and not exactly elegant. However if you have painful and swollen calves after a flight, it would be advisable to see a doctor.

- Make advance arrangements for oxygen if necessary. If you will need oxygen during your flight, check for airline availability, policies and cost well in advance, as some airlines do not carry any on board. If your airline does not, your doctor will need to provide a prescription and fill out an airline medical form that should be submitted at least three business days before your departure.
- If you are elderly or frail, ask your travel agent about tour operators who cater for the older traveller's specific needs, e.g. assistance with luggage and extended rest periods if required.
- In the event of a heart attack, you should know that portable defibrillators are becoming more widely available on most major airlines. Check with your airline to see if they already have defibrillators in place.
- The use of a GTN spray in a pressurised container for angina patients is safe to use during a flight but make sure you show it at the check-in desk to avoid any misunderstandings.
- Most major airlines can provide low-sodium, low-fat meals on flights with regular meal service if given 24-hours' notice. Many cruise lines can also provide these meals if notified in advance.

On your arrival

On arrival at your destination, you should be sure to pace yourself and avoid highly strenuous activities and unnecessary stress. Certain activities such as scuba diving, are extremely risky for heart patients and not recommended. If you take diuretics, stay hydrated, and try to monitor your salt intake when eating out. If you are taking blood thinners (such as warfarin), do not eat excessive amounts of green leafy vegetables. They contain high levels of vitamin K, which helps the blood to clot, and may interfere with the effectiveness of your medication. You should also be careful about the source of food and water you consume.

KEY TIPS

Don't be too macho (or the female equivalent thereof) to order wheelchairs in airports. This can be done at any time. If you are going to an unfamiliar airport, it is especially important because the walks can be very long. Security, immigration and customs queues are often quite long and slow. If you are in a wheelchair, you can handle such lines much faster and with less stress.

A porter will bring the chair and push you around in it. He should be tipped, except in Australia, New Zealand and some countries in the Orient where there is no tipping

If you need medical assistance in a foreign country, your hotel (assuming you are staying in one) can usually put you in touch with an English-speaking doctor who may even come to your room to see you. Foreign resort areas and cities often have clinics specialising in treating English-speaking tourists. Often the standard of care given by these clinics is good.

Cruise ships have infirmaries staffed by nurses and doctors. However, the quality of care is uneven. Sometime the ship's doctor is a retired physician who is given a free cruise in exchange for his services. On the newer and larger ships, the medical facilities and treatment are more likely to be professional than on smaller ships.

Passengers who are deemed seriously ill are usually removed from the ship at the first port of call - whether they want to be or not. You may find yourself in a hospital in Trinidad while your ship sails off into the sunset. In such a situation, good trip cancellation insurance is important because it will pay to get you home!

Before deciding whether you need trip cancellation insurance and how much, figure out how much of your trip's cost would be non-refundable if you had to cancel. Also figure the approximate cost of an unscheduled return. Tour and cruise operators impose cancellation penalties which increase as the departure date gets closer.

Cancellation penalties reach 100% of the total price at some point. The operators will show no mercy. You will not get a refund without cancellation insurance, whatever the circumstances. Most airline tickets are also non-refundable these days unless death occurs.

Basic health survival tips

Although you may decide that you do not want to push your luck by trying something too adventurous, there are a number of basic health rules that will help you to avoid getting sick on your travels, regardless of your basic heart condition.

Without wanting to frighten you, some bugs you pick up abroad can be with you for a long time. A friend got some type of dysentery when working as an archaeologist in Peru 15 years ago, and her bowel has never been the same since. On a cruise around the French Caribbean, I picked up a virus which led to damage to the cochlea in my ear (which controls your balance). Seven years later, I still suffer from dizziness and disorientation from time to time.

In some countries such as India and Mexico, the chances of avoiding a dodgy stomach are almost nil. I have visited Mexico many times, as a large part of my family live there. On several occasions, I have contracted what is known locally as Montezuma's Revenge, a particularly nasty form of diarrhoea, named after the sixteenth century Emperor of Mexico who was defeated by the Spaniards who then colonised the country.

However it does no harm to take whatever precautions you can, as there is nothing worse than getting stomach problems on top of your heart condition.

For a start, it is sensible to take a basic medical kit. Obviously you must be sure whether it is safe to take or use any of the following with your existing heart medications, but I have always found one or more of them very useful at various times on my travels:

- Insect repellent such as Repel 100 or Jungle Formula
- Antiseptic cream
- Sun/face cream and lip screen
- Throat lozenges
- Anti-diarrhoearal tablets such as Diocalm or Immodium
- A broad-spectrum antibiotic such as Ciproflaxin or Septrin, which covers a variety of infections. You will have to get these from a GP
- Analgesics such as aspirin or paracetamol. However, don't mix aspirin and warfarin. Don't use codeine-based

painkillers either
- Plasters, either moleskin or second-skin
- Oral re-hydration salts such as Dioralyte
- Dextrose glucose tablets
- Multi-vitamin tablets
- Iodine-based water purification tablets or a small bottle of tincture of iodine with a dropper.

Some of the information below will probably seem a bit over the top if you are walking in Scotland or the Pyrenees. But if you are heading off somewhere more exotic – and potentially dangerous from a health point of view – then do try and heed the advice as it comes from **Nomad Travel Stores & Clinics**. Nomad is one of the UK's best sources of equipment and survival information for those planning adventurous trips (*www.nomadtravel.co.uk*).

I am grateful to its Medical Director, Professor Larry Goodyer, for giving me this list of basic rules.

Cooker & utensils

If you are camping, it might be a good idea take your own cooker or Caricook, although if you are on an organised tour or expedition it shouldn't be necessary. If you do carry a cooker you will need cooking pots – mess tins are great as you can eat out of them and use them to store other bits and pieces. If you are really worried about hygiene you could also carry your own cup, plate and cutlery – this could save you a nasty stomach upset. Carrying your own eating and drinking utensils is still a good idea if you are staying in hostels. Don't get complacent if you are staying in a smart hotel. You can't see what's going on in the kitchens and many diseases are spread by kitchen/waiting staff's poor hygiene. However, I realise that you can't very well set out your own tableware in a restaurant – if you do, you may well be evicted and will certainly be subject to the strangest stares.

Water carriers

You should carry at least two litres of water at all times. The US Army bladder bottle is convenient because it compresses down when not in use, and is excellent for trekking. Otherwise take two one-litre bottles, one with an insulating cover. It's usually easy enough to buy bottled water in cities, but it's worth having at least a one-litre bottle for day trips or weekends out of the city.

Water purification
You will probably end up using a combination of bottled, tap and, if trekking, natural sources. If you are carrying your own cooker, you have the best method of sterilising to hand – boiling. Otherwise use a filter bag and iodine backed up with a small water purifier. (Also remember that the plastic bottles in which water is sold create a big disposal problem for developing countries, seriously polluting the environment.) It is recommend that you should take a bottle of iodine because it's so cheap and effective. If you're dying to drink the table water in a café or restaurant, check that it's clear, add iodine and it will be drinkable in 20–30 minutes. Alternatively, use the Aquapure system. It is simpler to drink bottled water but check that it is properly sealed and not brought open to the table, as it may well have been filled from a tap in less scrupulous restaurants.

Heat
It takes about three weeks for your body to fully acclimatise to hot and humid climates. Heat exhaustion and heatstroke are the most common illnesses caused by not drinking enough water and can lead rapidly to serious problems. The best way to avoid this is to drink small amounts frequently, certainly while on the move, and to stay out of direct sunshine – i.e. do everything you can to keep as cool as possible. It is therefore important that you have the facilities to carry and sterilise your water supply and add extra salt to your food.

Desert/Safari
Unlike in tropical climates, it is not as obvious how much body fluid you are losing by sweating in the desert or on safari, as it dries immediately in hot dry air. The rules are the same though: drink, drink, drink, even if you are not thirsty. Water is usually stored in large quantities for days in the desert. The best method is to treat the water once it has been decanted into your personal bottles.

Trekking
Trekking uses up a lot of energy and fluid, and you will sweat even in

cold environments. Even if you are not in the sun or heat, it is still very easy to dehydrate to a dangerous level. Once again, as for tropical conditions, keep drinking, drinking and drinking. You should get through at least six litres a day in cooler climates and up to ten litres in hot climates. Make sure you eat high-carbohydrate foods such as pasta, porridge and rice. During the day nibble regularly on biscuits, dried fruits and flapjack-style bars for more instant energy lifts. These foods will help you avoid exhaustion, which very easily leads to loss of concentration and therefore carelessness and accidents.

Food
You can eat most exotic foods if the following simple precautions are taken:

- Always eat freshly cooked dishes which are piping hot, peel-able fruits and vegetables or canned or packet food. Local dishes are usually safer than 'westernised' ones.
- Foods to avoid include salads, buffets, seafood, unwashed fruit and vegetables, unpasteurised dairy products and sauces.
- Cutlery or plates can often be dirty in restaurants so clean them with wet wipes before use.
- Do not be tempted to have ice in drinks and avoid ice cream made from an unsure water supply or with unpasteurised milk. Always clean your teeth in 'clean' water.
- Food prepared by yourself or your group is the safest of all. Wash fruit and vegetables in clean (boiled or treated) water. Do not allow persons with gut problems to prepare food.
- Always maintain a good standard of hygiene.

Medical supplies
It is usual for expedition organisers to provide the main medical kit. However, most expeditions will expect you to carry a small kit carrying more general items such as plasters, painkillers and any personal medication you may be taking. Gut infections often spread like wildfire in the closed circle of expedition groups – keep your

nails short, wash your hands frequently and use only your own eating and drinking equipment. In situations where you cannot wash properly, use wet wipes – don't let your personal hygiene slip.

Your kit needs to cover most minor eventualities including first aid, medication and creams, sterile equipment, rehydration and water purification. One of the all-in-one kits would be your best choice with malaria tablets added. You may want to consider carrying a malaria treatment if you are travelling off the beaten track more than 24 hours from reliable medical help.

In a city, you can get away with a much smaller kit. It's worth having the generic name of treatments and medication with you, should you need to buy from a local pharmacy. It's always worth carrying rehydration salts with you for travel to any hot country. If you plan to take short trips out of the city, you should consider a more comprehensive kit as well as a sterile kit. Facilities to ensure personal hygiene are readily available – your biggest threat is other peoples' lack of hygiene – so keep washing those hands.

If you are trekking, particular problems are blisters, exhaustion, altitude sickness, stomach upsets, dehydration, sprains and muscle pains, so your kit needs to be comprehensive. Pay attention to foot hygiene – a day's walking in thick socks and boots can easily lead to athlete's foot and infected blisters. If the environment allows it, wear sandals in the evening to air your feet.

Medical Supplies

Nomad and other suppliers offer a range of medical kits:

All-in-One Kits
All-in-one kits are designed to cover all the basic needs of travel health – first aid, sterile equipment, medication, water purification and rehydration.

First Aid Kits
First aid kits contain items for treating external injuries.

Medical Kit
Medical kits concentrate on stronger treatments you may need in

PERSONAL HYGIENE TOP TEN TIPS

1. Keep your nails short – trapped dirt can easily make its way into your mouth.
2. Avoid biting your nails.
3. Avoid putting objects such as pens/sunglasses in your mouth.
4. Wash your hands obsessively, particularly after shaking hands, opening doors and handling paper currency.
5. Use plenty of soap – water alone won't kill bacteria.
6. Use wet wipes when it is difficult to wash.
7. Avoid sharing clothing and equipment.
8. Pay attention to dental care.
9. Keep your clothes clean – stay in one place for a few days if you need to catch up with your laundry.
10. Frequently wash sweaty parts of the body to help avoid fungal infections.

more remote situations. Only buy them from reliable and well-equipped medical centres.

Sterile Kits
Carrying your own sterile equipment can save you from contracting diseases such as hepatitis B and HIV, particularly in countries where medical supplies are limited or non-existent and these diseases are prevalent. Sterile equipment is for you to hand over to a medical professional – it is not for your own use. Each kit contains a certificate of verification in four languages. The kits are graded according to how far from reliable medical help you intend to travel. They are packed in clear pouches for easy identification.

Possible Health Hazards

Insect borne diseases
A wide range of tropical diseases are spread by biting insects, the most dangerous to the traveller being malaria. Anti-malarial tablets are not 100% effective and you should take precautions against being bitten

by mosquitoes in malaria-endemic areas. Malaria is not the only potential problem so check with your GP or a specialised travel clinic which diseases are endemic to your trip.

Malaria
- The most dangerous disease to travellers, predominantly in the tropics
- Transmitted by female Anopheles mosquito which feeds from dusk to dawn

Areas affected
- South-East Asia, Pacific, Africa, South America

Prevention
- Use chemo prophylaxis (anti-malarials)
- Cover up with long sleeves, trousers and socks from dusk to dawn
- Use insect repellents
- Treat your clothing with a bug-proof clothing treatment
- Sleep under a treated mosquito net
- Carry standby malaria treatment with you if you are 24 hours away from medical help

Leishmaniasis
- Transmitted by sandfly
- Most active at dawn and dusk

Areas affected
- Southern Mediterranean, Middle East, Northern Africa, parts of Central Africa, South-East Asia

Prevention
- Sleep under a treated mosquito net (they will enter an untreated one)
- Sandflies find it hard to jump high so sleeping high up such as on the roof of a building is a good deterrent
- Use repellents
- Avoid moving around outside at dusk and dawn

Sleeping Sickness
- Transmitted by the Tsetse fly
- Feed during the daytime

- Attracted to dark blue clothing
- Attracted to fast moving objects such as a vehicle on safari

Areas affected
- Tropical Africa

Prevention
- Cover up with long sleeves, trousers and socks
- Repellents have some use, but are not always effective
- Treat your clothing with bug-proof clothing treatment
- In a vehicle, keep the windows closed and use a knock down spray containing Permethrin to kill any flies already there

Tick borne Encephalitis, Lyme Disease, Typhus
- All transmitted by ticks, which live in warm forested areas and moorland, but ticks carrying diseases affect most of the world

Prevention
- Cover up with trousers and socks
- Apply bug-proof clothing treatment to your socks and trousers
- When walking in suspect areas check regularly for ticks
- If an embedded tick is found, slowly pull the tick out with tweezers avoiding leaving any of it behind in the skin

Dengue Fever
- Transmitted by Aedes mosquito
- Daytime feeder

Areas affected
- South-East Asia, Pacific, Africa, Caribbean, South America, North Australia

Prevention
- Cover up with long sleeves, trousers and socks
- Use insect repellents
- Treat your clothing with bug-proof clothing treatment

Yellow Fever
- Transmitted by 'rain forest' and 'city' mosquito
- Feeds at any time

Areas affected
- Rain forest areas of South America and Central Africa

Prevention
- Vaccination – virtually 100% effective
- Use insect repellents

Onchocerciasis
- Parasitic worm transmitted by black fly
- Flies found near swiftly flowing rivers
- Can cause blindness if not treated

Areas affected
- Tropical Africa, Central & South America, Yemen

Prevention
- Avoid staying in such areas for long periods of time

General preventive measures
- Bug-proof clothing treatment works very effectively in conjunction with skin applied repellents
- Treated mosquito nets protect you even if there is a hole or you are touching the net when sleeping
- Burning coils are very effective for keeping insects away from you outside
- Knock down sprays are used to clear rooms or vehicles prior to entering
- Plug-ins are useful for clearing rooms where there is a reliable electricity supply
- Mosquito nets – essential in areas where insect borne diseases are endemic. Also use for a comfortable night's sleep where insects are a nuisance
- Head nets – use where insects are likely to swarm.

Travel/Health Insurance

Recent research carried out on behalf of the Foreign and Commonwealth Office shows that 71% of young people travelling abroad don't view insurance as being essential.

Whether you are 16 or 86, travel insurance *is* essential and you shouldn't even think about travelling without it. Otherwise you may be caught out in a foreign medical system, where you can be charged several thousand pounds for medical attention and then face a huge bill for getting home.

However, in the introduction to this book I warned that getting insurance can cause difficulties for those with heart conditions. Before setting off for two months in Australia recently I rang some insurance companies that offered specialist cover for those with pre-existing medical conditions. While not many turned me down, despite the fact that I have atrial fibrillation as well as having had a heart attack, the range of premiums ranged from the relatively modest to the outrageous.

I cannot believe that the risk I pose really justified the sort of premiums some companies demanded. Fortunately this was not true of some of the specialist operators who were generally very helpful and did not quote excessive premiums, given the circumstances. However you must be prepared to spend a long time on the phone answering seemingly endless medical questions, and you should keep your cool if you are either turned down or quoted a blood-pressure-raising premium.

Honesty is always the best policy. If in doubt as to whether a medical condition will be excluded or not, check with the potential insurer. There many common ailments that are classified as pre-existing medical conditions, which an insurer would need to know about before offering cover, ranging from heart problems through to those that you might not immediately think of like allergies, back problems, or even recurrent ear infections. For example, I was told by one household name that it wouldn't even cover people who were taking aspirin as a preventive measure in case of coronary disease, even if they did not have any actual problems.

It's also vital that if you have an automatically renewed annual travel policy, such as those offered 'free' with credit cards, to update the travel insurer about any conditions that have arisen since you took out the original policy.

Furthermore, most insurance companies insist that they also insure any family members travelling with you. This is because if you are taken ill while on holiday, the company can cover the costs of other members of the family who may have either to prolong their stay or fly home early with you.

Another problem area is buying insurance over the internet. If you apply for travel insurance online and say 'yes' when you are asked if you have any pre-existing conditions, then often you won't be given a quote.

If you are registered disabled, it is worth remembering that you have do have rights under the Disability Discrimination Act 1995. If you think that you have been discriminated against by an insurance company, refer to Part 3 of the Act which relates to 'service providers', including insurance and travel companies providing services within the UK.

Companies have a duty to make sure that, as a disabled customer, you are not unjustifiably treated less favourably than other customers, simply because you have a disability. The DDA states that it is against the law to refuse to provide a service to a disabled person which would be provided to other members of the public.

However, the law allows insurers to differentiate between disabled and non-disabled people. They may charge a higher premium, if they can show that it is a greater risk to insure a disabled person than a non-disabled person. The insurance company must be able to justify this difference by using accurate, relevant and reliable information and 'evidence'.

You can download the *Insurer's Guide to the Disability Discrimination Act 1995*, written by the **Association of British Insurers** (ABI) (*www.abi.org.uk*). If you're not happy with your insurance company, you can contact the **Financial Ombudsman Service** (*www.financial-ombudsman.org.uk*), which provides a free, independent service for resolving disputes with financial companies. It provides information in various formats including Braille and audio tape.

It is also important to remember that most insurers insist that you also obtain a European Health Insurance Card (EHIC) if you're going to a European Economic Area (EEA) country. The EEA consists of the European Union (EU) countries plus Iceland, Liechtenstein and Norway. Switzerland applies the EHIC arrangements through an agreement with the EU.

People who are ordinarily resident in the UK are entitled to a

UK-issued EHIC, but it is not valid for people who are going to live abroad. There are also some restrictions, depending on your nationality. UK and other EU nationals, as well as stateless persons and refugees, are covered in all EEA countries and Switzerland. Remember that the EHIC won't cover you if getting medical treatment is the main purpose of your trip.

The card replaces the old E111. You can apply for an EHIC:

- Online by visiting *www.dh.gov.uk/travellers*. Your card will be delivered within seven days.
- By calling the EHIC Applications Line on Tel: 0845 606 2030. Your card will be delivered within 10 days.
- By post – pick up an EHIC application pack from your local post office. Your card will be delivered within 21 days.

The EHIC is normally valid for three to five years and covers any medical treatment that becomes necessary during your trip, because of either illness or an accident. The card gives access to state-provided medical treatment only, and you'll be treated on the same basis as an 'insured' person living in the country you're visiting. Remember, this might not cover all the things you'd expect to get free of charge from the NHS in the UK. You may have to make a contribution to the cost of your care.

The EHIC also covers any treatment you need for a chronic disease or pre-existing illness. For limited information on oxygen supply services in the EEA countries and Switzerland, call the **Department of Health's Customer Service Centre** on tel: 020 7210 4850.

Chapter 4

Food for Your Heart

Heart-friendly – and not-so-friendly – cuisines around the world

I have already said that the first overseas trip I made after my heart attack was to a wedding anniversary celebration, held in a small town on the Slovak/Polish border. The local cuisine was rich, substantial and high in fat – a complete no-no for someone with heart problems.

So I have included here a chapter on countries with heart-friendly cuisines and those that might prove a bit more challenging. I have missed out the UK as I think most readers will be familiar with the heart hazards of our own cooking.

I would like to claim that I am an expert on all the world's major cuisines. Sadly this is not the case, although I have plenty of experience of dining on different continents. However, the main objective is to give a general idea of which countries' cuisines are easy on the heart, rather than providing a learned discourse on the finer points of global cooking. I trust, therefore, that readers with greater knowledge of a particular cuisine than mine, will be forgiving.

This chapter is a combination of my own knowledge, the picked brains of as many people as I know from different corners of the globe, and an extensive search of the web, including the work of the invaluable Sally Bernstein, whose website ***www.sallys-place.com*** contains a mine of information.

By way of general guidelines, you should try to eat principally fat that is mono-unsaturated and Ω-3 (or omega-3) polyunsaturated fatty acids (PUFA). The mono-unsaturated fats are found in olive oil and some other nut and vegetable oils and in dark, oily fish like herring, mackerel, sardines, sea bass, tuna and salmon.

These foods are important components of the Mediterranean

diet which, according to medical evidence, is probably a major factor in the low rates of cardiovascular disease of people living in Southern France, Italy, Greece and Spain.

Recently research has been carried out to find out whether the Mediterranean diet offers any benefit for those who have had a heart attack. More than 11,300 people were monitored for 3.5 years, and the researchers found that those who ate a Mediterranean-type diet were significantly less likely to die during the study period. So, given a choice between visiting Eastern or Southern Europe, both your head and your heart should tell you to go south.

If you have ever spent time in a coronary care unit, it is likely that you will have been visited by a dietician, given various booklets about diet and received a wagging finger from your cardiologist about the need to reduce weight and lay off the fags, booze and meat pies.

Then along comes a long-term study by the **American National Heart, Lung and Blood Institute** on the effects of low fat-diets on the health of middle-aged to elderly women. This study concluded that there was no statistical difference in incidences of heart disease and strokes between women who ate low-fat diets and those who ate whatever they wanted.

Now there seems to considerable dispute about the basis on which this study was carried out, so I think for the purposes of this book, we must assume that the advice given by the **British Heart Foundation** remains medically sound. The BHF advises that it's best to aim for a well-balanced, low-calorie diet. It should be low in saturated fat and high in fibre and include a range of fruit and vegetables. It maintains that if you combine this with regular exercise, your diet will be far more effective in the long term in managing coronary heart disease.

I have already pointed out that if you have a fairly delicate gut, travel can be a problem at the best of times. Strange foods, different time zones, dodgy hygiene and unusual meal patterns can play havoc with your digestive system. But when you also have to try to stick to a low-fat diet and keep the carbohydrates in check, day-to-day living can be quite a challenge.

However it is pure chauvinism to think that the UK has the upper hand when it comes to diet. Our high rate of heart disease is witness to that and Europeans often take a different view to us when it comes to diet. For example, in the UK and USA, the recent popularity of all things 'low carb' has sparked a backlash against potatoes, bread and pasta. The fear that Atkins and others have instilled in those who want to lose a few pounds has turned people against the very foods that most cultures view as healthy staples.

In contrast, for centuries, people along the coastal regions of the Mediterranean have enjoyed longer life expectancy and lower rates of heart disease and levels of cholesterol than their Northern European and American neighbours.

Wherever you travel, you need to be sensible about diet and it starts the minute you close your front door behind you and set off on your journey. Carolyn O'Neil and Denise Webb have written a best-selling book in the United States called *The Dish: On Eating Healthy and Being Fabulous* which gives very handy advice for heart travellers.

They point out that travelling by aeroplane is bound to be a day where you don't get the physical exercise you need, but your nerves will definitely get a work out. They warn:

> Get ready for the glamour of modern day travel – standing in security lines, waiting for delayed flights, jostling with fellow passengers to store your carry-on luggage, sitting on the runway, accepting an airline snack mix, and eventually making it to your destination.

> Air travel is in true survival mode these days and that means more people than ever are packing their own snacks and even meals to help get them through the day. At the same time airline meals are disappearing.

> Their top tips include:

> 1. Start the day ready for battle with a good breakfast including fibre rich and filling whole grain cereal or oatmeal and a big glass of orange juice. The hundreds of nutrients in OJ help boost your immune system to give you a fighting chance to ward off cold and flu germs floating in the cabin air on crowded flights.

2. Make your own Sky Trail Mix comprised of peanuts, almonds, raisins and other dried fruits. Healthy fats and stomach filling fibre will keep you going and this combo will be much lower in sodium than the on board snack mixes. You want to cut down on sodium intake today, because all that sitting can lead to unwanted puffiness and even ankle swelling.

3. If you are bored and have flipped through all of the magazines you've brought even before take off, you might be tempted to look to food for entertainment. So make sure to ask yourself if you really are famished.

4. If you are waiting for your flight at your normal mealtime, the good news is that most airports do have healthier choices today and some will pack it up for you to take on the plane in ready-to-fly containers. Many airports now have outlets selling freshly made sandwiches, salads, yoghurts and even sushi. A salad is fine, but make sure it contains some kind of protein, such as chicken, turkey, ham, eggs or cheese to keep your blood sugar on an even keel. Stress can take a toll, driving your blood sugar level down way below normal.

5. Be sure to stay hydrated. Dehydration can cause fatigue, headaches and irritability and you're already at risk for all three coping with flight delays, nowhere to recharge your laptop and people calling you on your mobile phone. Throw some bottled water in your bag. Many take-aboard suitcases have a special exterior pocket for bottled water.

Although it is not possible to examine the typical diet of every country you might want to visit, this chapter looks at eating habits in different parts of the world and, at risk of making some generalisations, offers broad guidelines on how to protect your heart from further unwarranted ravages.

There are, however, some general eating out tips which should help you wherever you go:

- Choose restaurants that have non-fattening foods on the menu
- Avoid buffets
- Refuse salad dressings and other sauces on the side
- Order grilled foods and ask that they be grilled without butter or oil
- Have tomato-based sauces with pasta rather than cream-based sauces
- Choose a broth rather than cream-based soup
- Drink water (provided it is bottled and obviously factory sealed) or diet drinks
- Share a starter and/or dessert if you are eating with someone else
- Order steamed vegetables
- Don't allow bread to be brought to the table before your meal is served
- Look for baked, grilled, dry-sautéed, broiled, poached or steamed foods (try to avoid or have less of: fried, basted, braised, au gratin, crispy, escalloped, pan-fried, sautéed, stewed or stuffed foods)
- Ask for low-calorie foods
- Stop eating when you are full.

Northern Europe

Belgium

Think Belgian food and drink and you normally think of mussels and chips with a blob of mayonnaise, heavy beers and delicious chocolate. While it is true that there are a lot of these around, Belgian cuisine is a bit more complex than this – though a bit heavy on the heart nonetheless.

Belgium is split down the middle between French and Flemish speakers and has been invaded and ruled by many other people – Romans, Vikings, French, Spanish, Austrians, Dutch, English and Germans. This has influenced their cuisine, and Belgians tend to say that their food is cooked with French finesse and served with German generosity.

Apart from its beer and *moules frites*, Belgium is also famous for its waffles and endive – though not necessarily eaten together! Beer laces the national dish, *carbonnades flamandes*, a Flemish beef stew.

Belgians love potatoes and are fond of game and meat. Charcuterie, a basket of bread, and beer often make a meal. Fish and seafood are important. Hearty soups play a big role, and the so-called *waterzooies* are the most typical. Almonds and spices are used in abundance.

While there are many excellent restaurants in Belgium, there is a great tradition of street food which mainly involves a paper cone of frites accompanied by mayonnaise, béarnaise or curry sauce or Belgian waffles stuffed with sugar. If you are looking after your heart, this street food is tempting but dangerous territory.

Netherlands

Dutch cuisine is not particularly distinctive, but it does consist of a bit more than the herring and cheese with which it is normally associated.

Inevitably the Netherlands has been exposed to the influence of other cuisines, in particular that of Indonesia. The traditional Indonesian *rijstafel* – or rice table – consists of around 11 dishes either served at your table or buffet style. You can also get vegetarian *rijstafel*, which is ideal if you are trying to cut down on the protein.

The Surinamese, Turkish and North African kitchens have also made their presence felt. However traditional Dutch meals are a bit more challenging to the heart. Breakfast usually consists of bread, thin slices of Dutch cheese, cured meats and sausage, butter and jam or honey, and often a boiled egg. A working lunch may be *koffietafel*, once again with breads, cold meat, cheese and pickles. There will often be a side dish of omelette or salad. The most common daytime snacks are *broodjes* (sandwiches) served in the ubiquitous sandwich bars – *broodjeswinkels*. Filled pancakes are also popular. Lightly salted 'green' herring can be bought from street stalls.

More substantial dishes are generally reserved by the Dutch themselves for the evening meal: *erwtensoep* (thick pea soup served with smoked sausage, cubes of bacon, pig's knuckle and brown or white bread), *groentensoep* (clear consommé with vegetables, vermicelli and meatballs), *hutspot* (potatoes, carrots and onions), *klapstuk* (brisket of beef) and *boerenkool met rookworst* (kale and potatoes served with smoked sausage). Seafood dishes are often excellent, particularly in Amsterdam or Rotterdam, and include *gebakken zeetong* (fried sole), *lekkerbekjes* (fried whiting), royal imperial oysters, shrimps, mussels, lobster and eel cooked in a variety of ways. Dutch desserts are generally best avoided from a calorie point of view.

France

The first time I encountered garlic was when I was ten years old, back in the 1950s, where my mother took my sisters and I to a small seaside town in Normandy where my grandmother worked as a travel courier. Although it was nearly 50 years ago, I can still taste that exotic and unfamiliar flavour, so unlike the bland post-war stodge we had to contend with back home.

French cuisine, particularly in the North, is potentially bad news for those with heart problems. Although the French are becoming more health conscious and certainly drink less than they used to, their typical diet is laden with cream, butter, full-fat cheese, bread, red meat and chocolate. Yet the paradox is that the French are in general quite *svelte* and have far fewer problems with heart disease than we do.

No one is quite sure why this is – but it makes the French, not unjustifiably, feel somewhat smug as they see us Brits struggle with our weight, while eating no more fat and carbohydrates than they do.

It may be something to do with all those suppositories they like to insert in themselves or, more likely, that they are simply far more fussy about the quality and freshness of the food they eat and would not be seen dead eating some of the low-grade processed junk we tend to pick off the shelves.

Fruits and vegetables are used liberally in meals – although tinned peas turn up more often than you would imagine and some of the salads can look suspiciously commercial. Poultry and pork tend to be free-range, although having lived in the French countryside for some years, I am slightly dubious of French farmers' claims that their products are free of hormones and pesticides.

Another possible reason for the French diet paradox is that portions tend to be smaller than in the UK and certainly than in the USA. After all, *nouvelle cuisine* was invented in France and even though the French may consume richer foods, they actually take in fewer calories, and rarely snack throughout the day. Despite this, French supermarkets are as piled high with crisps, snacks and garish fizzy drinks as their counterparts in the UK.

France, despite the reputation for its overall cuisine, has considerable variations from one part of the country to another. For example, the food of Northern France has a strong Flemish influence with beef cooked in stout and *andouillete*, a type of sausage with just about every part of the animal thrown in. *Boucheries Chevalines* (horse meat butchers) are common in France – but particularly in the North – and for us sensitive souls, it is necessary to ensure you are not eating horse burgers.

In Mediterranean areas such as Provence, olives and seafood are prevalent. In the wine-producing regions of Burgundy and Bordeaux, inevitably wine is prevalent in the cooking process, while Normandy cooks use lashings of butter, cream, cheese, apples and seafood.

Some French food is not for the squeamish. The French are not afraid to eat anything. Kidney, brain, sweetbreads, tripe, blood sauces and sausages, sheep's foot, tongue and intestines are all common in Gallic cooking and hold equal standing with lamb, beef, pork, poultry and game.

With the exception of a few big city restaurants, vegetarianism is considered a deviancy. A vegetarian friend once asked for a quiche lorraine and checked with the waiter that it was meat-free. When it arrived, it was packed with bacon so she gently remonstrated. The waiter simply shrugged his Gallic shoulders and said 'bacon isn't meat'. Try telling that to the poor old dead porker!

Germany

I have a soft spot for German food as my mother came from Southern Germany and she used to cook several German dishes at a time when British food was bland at best, and disgusting at worst. However you do need to be careful, as it is really not the most heart-friendly cuisine on the continent.

Certainly traditional German cuisine and eating habits are a challenge to those – let alone those with heart problems – who are trying to watch their weight. Unlike the French, you can see where the Germans put their food and drink.

German cuisine varies greatly from region to region. Generally speaking, the southern regions of Bavaria and Swabia have the heaviest cuisine, while western parts have some French influence. Eastern parts have more in common with their old Iron Curtain counterparts, as opposed to Northern Germany where Scandinavian influences are prevalent.

Germany boasts at least 300 different types of bread, ranging from white wheat bread to grey bread (*graubrot*) and black (actually dark brown) rye bread (*schwarzbrot*). Most types of bread contain both wheat and rye flour (hence *mischbrot*, mixed bread), and often wholemeal and seeds as well. *Pumpernickel*, a Westphalian black bread, is not baked but steamed, and has a unique sweetish taste.

Breakfast *(frühstück)* commonly consists of bread, toast and/or bread rolls (*brötchen* or *semmeln*) with jam, marmalade or honey, eggs and coffee (cocoa for children). Ham and salami are also commonly eaten on bread in the morning, as are various cheeses. A variety of meat-based spreads such as *Leberwurst* (liver sausage) are often on the breakfast table as well as muesli and cornflakes.

Traditionally, the main meal of the day is lunch (*mittagessen*), eaten around noon. Dinner (*abendessen* or *abendbrot*) is a smaller meal, sometimes only consisting of a couple of sandwiches. However, altered working habits have forced this to be changed in recent decades. Today, it is not uncommon for many Germans to eat their main meal in the evening.

Pork is the most popular meat, but you will find plenty of poultry such as duck and goose and game such as boar, rabbit and venison. Meat is usually pot-roasted while in the fish department, trout, pike, carp and perch are all popular, as well as pickled herrings.

The real killers are the wide variety of cakes and tarts. However they are often made with fresh fruit such as apples, plums, strawberries and cherries, which is some compensation. A particularly calorific cheesecake is also very popular.

Slightly less death-defying is a popular dessert in northern Germany called *rotegrütze*, red fruit jelly, which is cooked from black and red currants, raspberries and sometimes with strawberries or cherries. It is traditionally served with cream, but also common with custard or whipped cream. *Rhababergrütze* (rhubarb jelly) and *grüne grütze* (gooseberry fruit jelly) are variations of the *rotegrütze*.

Scandinavia

The thing that is most likely to make your heart go boom in Scandinavia (Norway, Sweden, Denmark and Finland) is the price rather than the nature of the food you eat. Scandinavian fare isn't the most spectacular in Europe, but you can always get a good if expensive meal. There are very good vegetarian restaurants, and many have extensive hot and cold buffets which are safe to eat because Scandinavian hygiene standards are very high. This makes it easy to ensure you are eating a healthy and safe diet.

Scandinavian cuisine has varied staple ingredients – fish, pork and poultry, as well as beetroot, potatoes, cucumbers, dill, parsley and horseradish and boiled, baked or smoked apples.

The Viking favourites of oysters and mussels as well as mutton, cheese, cabbage, apples, onions, berries and nuts, continue to be staples of the Scandinavian diet. Some of the more esoteric tastes of the Vikings live on. The Norwegians insist that a whale steak, properly marinated and broiled, can taste as good as beef. Some Swedes rave about smoked horse flesh, which they refer to as 'hamburger' and buy thinly sliced.

Scandinavia's isolation inevitably helped spawn many local dishes and traditions. Out of the far north has come one of the greatest Scandinavian delicacies, cured salmon, which is prepared with sugar, salt, white pepper and dill.

If many of the foods of the area have a salty or smoky taste, or are pickled or dried, it's largely because of winter. The preservation of foods was the only kind of life insurance that Scandinavians used to have.

Scandinavian food might not be to everyone's taste, but it is certainly healthy and should cause you no problems. However, all those long dark winter days are not great for your mental health. So I suggest you stick to the long summers, even though dark-free nights can be an unsettling experience, and your pocket will certainly end up light, whatever the time of year!

Eastern Europe

Czech Republic

The old Eastern Bloc countries offer a real challenge for those of us nursing dodgy hearts. Indeed I would go as far as to say that although Prague is beautiful, it is now a place to be approached warily with its pickpockets, hordes of drunken Brits on stag or hen parties and really challenging cuisine. However don't let me put you off. You can overcome the food challenges by careful choices and if you leave anything of value in your hotel safe, muggers will at least leave empty handed. Sadly, though, the drunken Brits just keep coming and spoiling the party.

So what do I mean by 'challenging' food? When you buy a 'salad' at a deli, for example, what you often get is a very thick mayonnaise-based dressing and small pieces of vegetables and meat. Vegetarianism is only recently catching on in Central Europe, so there aren't many options, unfortunately. But if you like beetroot, turnips, carrots, onions and potatoes, you're in luck.

Czech food is rich and hearty, but if you've never tried it, there are a few things worth knowing. The *knedlik* is the most common side dish. It is a dumpling, made of either wheat or potato and served with gravy. Most dishes consist of pork or beef, but chicken, turkey, freshwater fish, duck, lamb and rabbit are common, too. Play safe with *spis,* similar to a shish kebab, with grilled meat and vegetables on a spear.

Czechs like sugar in just about everything, it seems. Sauces, gravies and salad dressings are uncommonly sweet. Otherwise food can be quite bland. Most dishes come with *zeli* or cabbage, while many things are marinated – so if you don't like vinegar, life is going to be tough. The Czechs like their bread dry and chewy; I can't say I share their taste in that department.

Slovakia

Slovak food is often described as 'hearty and filling'. For which read *very tough on the ticker!*

The best-known Slovak soup is *kapustnica*, a cabbage soup with smoked pork sausage that often contains mushrooms, and sometimes plums, especially at Christmas. Another typical Slovak soup is *fazulova polievka*, made of beans and root vegetables such as carrots and parsley. Sometimes, smoked pork is added. Best for the heart would be *cesnakova polievka*, a garlic soup usually cooked in chicken broth with parsley and an egg, or croutons.

A very typical Slovak starter is a slice of ham stuffed with horseradish flavoured cream. Another popular but horribly fatty starter is *bryndza*, which is cheese in pastry dough or flavoured with paprika and served with bread.

Miesany salat (mixed salad) is readily available in Slovakia but watch out for the word *sterilizovany*, which indicates that the vegetables are tinned.

Side dishes, such as rice or potatoes, are usually not included in the price of your main course in restaurants and need to be ordered separately. Mashed potatoes (*zemiakova kasa*), baked potatoes (*zapekane zemiaky*), French fries (*hranolky*), boiled potatoes (*varene zemiaky*), fried potatoes similar to home fries without onions (*opekane zemiaky*) and potato croquettes (*zemiakove krokety*) are the most common potato side orders.

Rice is served plain (*obycajna*) or flavoured with ham (*sunka*), curry (*kari*), peas (*hrasok*), or mushrooms (*hriby*). Some restaurants serve dumplings (*halusky*) as a side dish.

Bryndzove halusky are dumplings with melted feta cheese and fried bacon sprinkled on the top. These are often considered the national dish and are usually the least expensive item on the menu. Bizarrely, they are sometimes listed in the dessert section. Another traditional dish is dumpling with cabbage and bacon.

Other than salads, vegetarians will plough a lonely furrow. Often, the only items are cheeses, fried mushrooms, fried cauliflower or omelettes. Fried cheese (*vyprazany syr*) is also available but guaranteed to raise cholesterol in a flash.

Poland

With the recent arrival of so many Polish workers in the UK, supermarkets and corner shops are rapidly filling their shelves with their favourite foods. I have to say, however, that the sausages, bread and cakes all look pretty tough on the digestion.

Polish cuisine is a mixture of Slavic and foreign traditions. Meats of all kinds predominate as well as noodles and dumplings, the most notable of which are the *pierogi*. These are semi-circular dumplings of unleavened dough stuffed with anything from sauerkraut and hard boiled eggs to meat and fruits. As they are normally deep-fried, they are a bit of a no-go zone, but they do come boiled as well which may be safer for coronary cases.

A typical lunch is often made up of four courses, starting with a soup, followed by salmon or herring prepared in either cream, oil or vinegar. The main course may be the national dish, *bigos* (sauerkraut with pieces of meat and sausage) or a breaded pork cutlet. Meals often finish with home-made poppy seed cake.

There are many locally made dishes specific to different parts of Poland. Fresh-water fish is the favourite dish in the north of Poland, the centre of the country specialises in *Zurek,* a sour rye soup, while in the North you will find aromatic duck dishes. At the foot of the Tatra mountains, *kapusniak* – (sauerkraut soup) and *oscypek* (a sheep's milk smoked cheese) are very popular.

Hungary

Many think that Hungarians eat heavy, fatty dishes, a key ingredient of which is the throat-burning hot red paprika. However, the official line is that this is old hat and that lard has long been dumped for vegetable oil. They also maintain that red paprika is only used to enhance the flavour of the dishes.

As always, the truth is probably somewhere in the middle, but with care, it is perfectly easy to manage heart-friendly meals, particularly in Budapest.

Probably *ghoulash* is the best known dish, but contrary to popular belief, the real thing is not a stew but a thick soup. Sour cream is used a lot, but there are plenty of not-too-rich dishes such as fish soup, chicken paprika, home-made *pörkölt* (stew) and excellent fresh-water fishes such as grilled pike, perch and trout. There are probably lots of good ethical as well as fitness reasons for not eating the Hungarian favourite – goose liver, particularly when it is fried. To my eternal shame, I once wrote a booklet for the French cooperative of goose liver producers, and I felt quite sick just reading about the way the poor geese are force fed to artificially inflate their livers.

Desserts in Hungary are a bit of a no-go area, I'm afraid. However, if your resistance weakens, the most delicious ones are *strudels, Gundel* pancakes, *somlói* dumplings and *gesztenyepüré* (cooked chestnuts mashed, topped with whipped cream). For pure curiosity, you could try *túrós csusza* (pasta with curd and sour cream).

Russia

I first went to Moscow when it was warily opened up to tourists in the early 1970s. The food was virtually inedible and served half-cold. I couldn't identify most of the dishes, but you had to arrive exactly on time for meals as the surly waiters delivered all three courses at the same time, regardless of whether you were actually at the table.

While things have obviously vastly improved, the fact remains that Russia is mainly a northern country with long cold winters. Therefore food is designed to give as much energy and warmth as possible and is thus heavier on carbohydrates and fat than lean protein. You will find potatoes of all kinds (boiled, fried, baked, chipped, potato pancakes, potato soup, mashed potato, etc.), lots of bread, eggs, pork and beef, liberal use of butter, honey, sugar – a true recipe for heart attacks.

A main meal in Russia will usually consist of soup, perhaps some salad and a main meat/vegetable dish such as *beef stroganoff* and *blinis* (sweet pancakes) followed by tea.

Obviously Moscow and St Petersburg are more sophisticated than rural areas or small towns. In Moscow you can pretty much eat anything you want – but at a cost. Of course the old Soviet Union has now been broken up into several countries, whose cuisines vary considerably from each other. I do not have the space to consider them individually, but some will obviously be more heart-friendly than others. Take Russia's southern neighbour Georgia, for example.

Despite some heart-busting specialities like *khachapuri*, a cheese-filled baked bread sometimes served with an egg, and *khinkali*, which are giant boiled dumplings, the hallmark of the Georgian national cuisine is fresh ingredients. The basic flavours come from walnuts and hazelnuts, pomegranates and plums and herbs. There are also spices, notably in dishes from the western Georgian regions such as Mingrelia.

A typical Georgian meal will begin with aubergine stuffed with ground walnut paste or fried aubergine with sweet pepper, air-dried beef and minced spinach with walnuts. It may be followed by *shashlik* of marinated grilled meats, served with a range of sauces such as *ajika*, which uses chilli peppers, or stews such as *chakhokhbili* or chicken with herbs and *chanakhi* with mutton and aubergine.

Southern Europe
Greece

Although Greek food is generally pretty healthy, tourist restaurants tend to produce rather greasy food, some of which can be quite unappetising. Furthermore, it is usually served lukewarm. However, sauces are reasonably heart-friendly because they are normally based on wine, stocks, tomato and yoghurt, rather than butter or cream. Lentils and beans are commonly used in starters and main courses, and vegetables feature prominently in starters, soups and main courses.

Watch out for *tarmasalata*, the pink coloured, cream-based cod roe dip, which is very calorific. It is better to stick to *tzatziki*, made with yoghurt, garlic and cucumber, or *hummus,* which consists of sesame paste and chickpeas. If you order soup, try *torato*, which is cold soup with eggplant, peppers and yoghurt. This has more fibre and less cholesterol than the ubiquitous *avgolemono* soup, which has a lemon and egg base.

It may also be better to pass up on *moussaka* which is made from eggs and cheese and stick to grilled meat such as *souvlaki*, which is lamb marinated in lemon juice, olive oil and herbs and then skewered and grilled. Other safe bets are fish in *plaki* sauce made with tomatoes and garlic, or *dolmas,* which are vine leaves stuffed with ground meat, rice and pine nuts. Because they're steamed or baked, there is usually no added fat when they are cooked.

Greek salads usually contain olives and *feta* cheese, which are both high in sodium. You can always ask to have the *feta* rinsed before it is served but I suspect that you might get some funny looks.

Italy

Despite what I have said about healthy Mediterranean food, Italian cooking can have its danger points and you certainly see plenty of substantial Italian mammas around.

To start with, you need to differentiate between Northern and Southern Italian cuisines. Southern Italy traditionally follows a Mediterranean diet, which is rich in grains, fruits and vegetables, contains very little meat and uses olive oil in place of butter. Northern Italian cuisine, on the other hand, is heavy on beef, veal, butter and cream. In the far North you will find plenty of fattening things like *gnocchi*, which are little potato dumplings.

But you can eat healthily even in a Northern Italian-style restaurant by skipping the ravioli, *pasta Alfredo* and other cheese-filled pastas in favour of pasta with red clam sauce or meat sauce. Remember that a standard antipasto contains heavily smoked and salted meats and cheeses. Opt instead for a green salad (*insalata)* or tomato and mozzarella salad (*panzanella).* Instead of veal or chicken *piccata, marsala* or *saltimbocca,* try grilled meat or poultry, fish *in cartoccio* (baked in parchment) or marinated squid. For dessert, resist the *cannoloni* or cream-filled pastry. Instead, order an Italian ice or fresh fruit.

Spain

Spanish cuisine reflects the diverse history and geography of the country itself. In Andalusia, for instance, you will often find oriental-style flavours with liberal use of spices and herbs, oranges and other fruits in savoury dishes.

In the far north of Spain, by contrast, the cuisine features peasant dishes of beans, sausages and vegetables as well as some of Spain's best seafood. The east coast of Spain, facing Italy, encompasses the regions of Catalonia, Valencia and Murcia. Valencia is the home of *paella,* Spain's best-known dish, which normally consists of saffron rice mixed with various shellfish, although it is sometimes served with chicken.

Castile, Extremadura, La Mancha and Aragón are famous for baby lamb and suckling pig, done to a turn in wood-fired brick ovens. With nearly 2,000 kilometres of coastline, Spain also has plenty of fresh seafood.

In spite of the diversity of the cuisine, several dishes appear everywhere in Spain. One is the *tortilla* (nothing to do with the Mexican tortilla), which is a round, flat omelette made with chopped potatoes. Originally, *tapas* were simply a few olives or almonds, and perhaps a selection of cheeses, sausages and serrano ham, and possibly cubes of tortilla served, often free, with a glass of fino sherry. Nowadays, *tapas* include any hot or cold dish that can be served in small portions. They are displayed along the length of the counter of a bar or café and you then order them in a group, or individually. They are particularly good for heart care, as you can pick and choose a selection of low-fat dishes and ignore the more fatty fried fish and lamb.

Serrano and *iberico ham* (salt–cured ham served raw and very thinly sliced) is a basic staple of *tapas* as well as with Andalusian olives, alongside a variety of salads, fresh anchovies (*boquerones*) and rings of squid (*calamares*), chunks of fresh hake and a variety of seafood. There are also often hot dishes such as grilled pork loin, kidneys, mushrooms, lamb stew and broad beans with ham.

(Thanks for some of this information are due to Janet Mendel, the American cookery writer who has written many books on Spanish cooking: **www.andalucia.com/taste/janet.htm**.*)*

North Africa

Morocco, Tunisia, Egypt and now to a lesser extent Libya, have become popular tourist destinations. Popular dishes include slow-cooked spicy stews and aromatic *tagines*, such as *harissa* and *berbere*, *couscous*, and pastries dipped in honey and flower essences.

I must confess to finding it hard to think kindly about Moroccan cuisine after spending nearly a month in bed with dysentery after eating a dodgy meal in a souk in Tangier – given that that was forty years ago, perhaps I should give it another try!

A generally heart-friendly cuisine, the North African diet contains lots of fresh vegetables, grains, nuts and seeds, although *merguez*, a very popular sausage, contains a lot of fat.

North African meals range from simple and non-spicy to complex and hot. Communal eating is common, with lots of dishes served on the table. All North African regions have stews, charcoal-grilled meats, vegetable dishes and very rich, sweet pastries.

Religious cooking and the dietary restrictions practised by Muslims and Coptic Christians have greatly influenced North African cuisine. In particular, the Muslims' use of nuts in sauces, saffron to scent rice and couscous, floral essences to flavour desserts, and spiced teas and coffees, show up throughout the region. Likewise you generally won't find pork because of Muslim dietary laws.

A North African day begins with a breakfast of bread, grains, beans, vegetables and/or cheese, depending on where you are. Breakfast may include croissants with cheese or ham, fruit, porridge made from millet or chickpea flour, flatbread with grilled vegetables, crispy fried *fava* bean cakes with *tahini* sauce, *hummus*, salad or fluffy pastry with vegetables or chicken – a truly all day breakfast. However don't be surprised if you are only offered a French-style Continental breakfast.

In Morocco, lunch typically begins with spiced tomato and cucumber, grilled vegetables and chickpeas, followed by vegetable or fish soup, noodles, or *tagines,* accompanied by salad and bread or pasta.

In Tunisia, lunch can include *brik*, a thin, savoury pancake filled with spinach, mashed potato and soft boiled egg or sandwiches made with tuna, hard-boiled eggs, peppers, diced tomatoes, onions and olive oil with a touch of *harissa*. In Egypt, lunch may consist of stews, kebabs, falafel or breads with *hummus*.

Dinner is the main meal of the day in many regions. *Mezzas* are served as starters, including lamb kebabs, pickled olives, cheese, savoury pastries, fried cheese, grilled chickpeas or sardine fritters, followed by chicken, fish or meat with *couscous*, pasta or bread. Pudding is usually fresh or dried fruits, sometimes, followed by sweet pastries or almond biscuits.

Sadly, it is probably better to avoid the sweet, rich North African desserts that include *briks* (sweet fritters of dried fruits), *kab el ghzal* (horn-shaped pastry with almond paste), *konafa* (nuts, sugar and shredded wheat), *fatirs* (pancakes stuffed with eggs or apricots), *baklava* (flaky pastry with chopped nuts and saturated with honey) and *makhroud* (semolina cakes or cookies stuffed with dates and soaked in honey-orange flower water).

Sub Saharan Africa

Certain regions are distinctive for the development of indigenous cuisine or incorporation of outside influences, including Ethiopia, Nigeria, East and West Africa, the former Portuguese colonies of Angola and Mozambique and South Africa.

Mealie, the African name for corn, is used to make the soft cornmeal mush and batters that are a characteristic of African food. *Fufu* is a stiff corn meal or yam mush. Porridges and ground millet, sorghum, teff, barley and cassava flour make up the typical fritters, batters, flatbread and griddlecakes.

The prime characteristic of native African meals is the use of starch filler foods, accompanied by a stew containing meat or vegetables. Cassava and yams are main root vegetables. Steamed greens, mixtures of hot spices with root vegetables and stew are normally on the menu. Peanuts, called groundnuts in Africa, feature heavily in many dishes. Melons, particularly watermelon, are popular.

Ethiopia

Removed geographically from the rest of Africa, Ethiopia has one of the purest indigenous cuisines on the continent. Its high interior plains, cool nights and long growing season provide an abundant variety of food, even though this will be at variance with the image many British people have of Ethiopia as blighted by famine.

While this is undoubtedly true – tragically so – to an extent, it belies the rich Ethipoian culinary tradition. Ethiopians have a meat-based diet and are very particular about its freshness. A popular dish is a local version of steak tartare. Accompanying many dishes is the fiery *berbere*, a spicy hot pepper paste. *Doro wat*, a stewed chicken, is the national dish. *Teff*, the smallest form of millet, is ground into flour, used in a thin fermented batter to make *injera,* which is a circular flatbread.

Nigeria/West Coast

Nigeria and the coastal parts of West Africa are fond of chillies in food. Coastal recipes include fish marinated in ginger, tomatoes and cayenne. There is a French influence in Senegal, which uses touches of lime juice, chopped vegetables including scallops, garlic and marinades. Peanut oil, palm oil, and often coconut oils are common. The black-eyed pea is a staple of West Africa and native okra is used in many dishes to thicken soups and stews. Tropical fruits, particularly bananas and coconuts, are important ingredients.

In West African cuisine, croquettes of yams, fried in peanut oil, along with bananas and plantain, are important parts of the local diet. Yams are often served with eggs.

The cooking of West Africa often combines fish and meat. Flaked and dried fish is browned in oil and combined with chicken, yam, onions, chilli oil and water to make a highly flavoured stew. Beef and mutton are not commonly eaten in West Africa, as they tend to be very tough.

East Africa

East Africa is huge – Kenya, for example, is larger than France – so any survey of its cuisine attempted here will be necessarily partial and will not do full justice to regional variations and traditions. The diet is again starch-based, with millet, sorghum, bananas and milk, mostly found as curds and whey. Cornmeal is now such a basic part of African cuisine that it is hard to believe that it was originally a New World import.

Home to some of the greatest game reserves, East African cuisine is distinctive for the almost total absence of meat. Cattle, sheep and goats are regarded as more a form of currency and status, and so are not eaten. The Masai live almost entirely upon the milk and blood, but not the meat, of their cattle.

Settlers influenced East Africa by importing their cuisine almost in its entirety. The first settlers were the Arabs, settling in the coastal areas. The many *pilaf* dishes, rice cooked in the Persian steamed and spiced manner, are still widely eaten. Pomegranate juice, saffron, cloves, cinnamon and allspice are all found in East African food, showing its Arabic influences. Many centuries later, the British, and their imported workers from India, conspired to forever influence the East African diet, introducing boiled vegetables and curries.

The Portuguese influence upon Angola and Mozambique is pervasive and subtle. They were the first Europeans to move to Africa south of the Sahara in the fifteenth century. Settling so long ago, the Portuguese influenced African culinary life to a greater extent than the more direct and intrusive British, French and Dutch. Just as in their Indian colony of Goa, the Portuguese brought the European sense of flavouring with spices, and techniques of roasting and marinating to African foods. These influences blended with local cuisines and ingredients to produce subtle and aromatic recipes. Separated across the tip of the continent, Mozambique's diet is more fish-based. Angola, on the other hand, has a diet more akin to West African countries.

The Portuguese introduced citrus fruits as well as chillies, peppers, corn, tomato, pineapples, bananas and the domestic pig. In addition to growing cashews, Mozambique is most known for its *piripiri*, or hot pepper dishes.

South Africa

South Africa's history has led to the emergence of a polyglot cuisine. European colonisation, the adaptation of the native Bantu cooking, and large-scale immigration of foreign workers, have all contributed. Dutch settlers brought their forms of agriculture, and the British merchants imported the mixed grills that now include African game meats.

Malay workers contributed curries, adding spice to a plain English-Dutch influence. British Empire Indians who came to build the railroads, forever influenced cuisine with dal, lentil soups and curries. Game and lamb, lobster, and a variety of fish add to a cosmopolitan cuisine. In the bush and smaller towns with mostly native Africans, the main meals remain stew-based. South Africa's most unusual meat is called *biltong*, a spicy form of wind-dried jerky.

North America

United States

There are two major difficulties for those with heart problems visiting the United States. First, travel insurance can be extremely expensive; second, the typical US diet is a killer – literally. Here are some alarming facts from the US Surgeon General:

- 61% of adults in the United States are overweight or obese.
- 13% of children aged 6 to 11 years and 14% of adolescents aged 12 to 19 years are overweight. This prevalence has nearly tripled for adolescents in the past two decades.
- These increases in being overweight or obese cut across all ages, racial and ethnic groups, and both genders.
- 300,000 deaths each year in the United States are associated with obesity.
- Being overweight or obese are associated with heart disease, certain types of cancer, Type 2 diabetes, stroke, arthritis, breathing problems and psychological disorders, such as depression.

Apparently there are 75 official competitive eating competitions in the US, which are sanctioned, would you believe, by the

International Federation of Competitive Eating – with £84,000 prize money at stake. Many of the competitions are screened on the sports channel ESPN, and they are watched by millions of guzzlers. The IFCE is even lobbying for competitive eating to be included in the Olympics.

If you are simply making a trip to the United States, you will probably not have time to accumulate a lot of excess weight, let alone take part in competitive gorging. Furthermore, many Americans are actually very diet-conscious, and although the general size of the population might indicate weak will power, there are plenty of low-fat and low-carb options available if you can resist the jumbo portions of fat and calorie-loaded food that are offered everywhere.

The first time I went to the United States was in the 1960s. The sheer volume of food blew my mind even though it didn't seem to taste of very much. I arrived as a skinny schoolboy weighing just over ten stone. I left a year later, a plump youth hitting thirteen stone, and I have had weight problems ever since.

While the majority of the United States' population is made up of 'white' descendants of European settlers, it is also home to millions of Puerto Ricans, Cubans, Indians, Native Americans and African-Americans. The result is an extraordinarily varied cuisine, even though we tend to think that classic American food consists of burgers and fries, chilli dogs, ice-cold fizzy drinks and milkshake. Fast food is a true culinary tradition in the United States. It was the birthplace of **McDonald's**, **In-n-Out Burger**, **Fat Burger**, **Tommy's**, **Taco Bell**, and many other fast-food chains, now at once iconic and reviled.

However there is a strong regional cuisine in the United States, influenced by the culinary heritage of the groups that first settled there. Characteristic ingredients of New England cooking include seafood, cranberries, rhubarb and apples. Heavily influenced by British settlers, cooking techniques in New England rely on roasting and boiling to produce such dishes as clam chowder, baked beans and salt cod.

The southern states were influenced by French, English and Spanish colonists and by African slaves, who often served as household cooks and who introduced okra, black-eyed peas and eggplant to the menu. The region is fertile ground for rice, which is featured in the classic southern rice pudding. Other typical dishes include fried green tomatoes, squash casserole, fried chicken, cornbread and grits.

The midwest is known for corn, beef and dairy produce, and the region's cooking techniques reflect the influence of German and Scandinavian settlers. Traditional dishes include beef pot roast, *bratwurst*, *sauerkraut* and corn-on-the-cob. In the southwest, where Spanish and Mexican influences predominate, typical ingredients include chillies, cumin, cinnamon, tortillas and tomatoes. Barbecuing is the best-known cooking technique, and common dishes include many Tex-Mex interpretations of Mexican cooking. The Pacific northwest is known for seafood, game and berries. Dishes identified with the Pacific northwest include salmon, venison, pumpkin soup and gooseberry relish.

California is probably the best place to protect your heart. San Francisco and LA are phenomenally health conscious, and you should have no difficulty in keeping the fat at bay.

Central America

Mexico

As I said earlier, I have visited Mexico several times, since for complicated political and historical reasons, my mother's sister settled there in the 1940s. She arrived there with help from Albert Einstein (an extremely distant relative but good friend of my grandparents), after a spell in hiding in a nunnery in Lourdes. Once there, she begat an unusual family, which now includes soap opera stars, a ballet dancer, a brain surgeon and a physicist. I love visiting them, though I am always in fear of the dreaded *Montezuma's Revenge* which has struck me several times.

Furthermore, Mexican food, though often delicious, is not always compatible with healthy eating. Although staples of Mexican food such as corn *tortillas*, beans and rice are excellent sources of complex carbohydrates, they tend be prepared with lots of fat and salt.

Tacos and *tortillas* are sometimes, but not always, deep-fried and cheese and sour cream toppings add more fat and calories. But, if you apply the trusty principles of balance and moderation, you can still eat healthily.

As a rule, foods that are prepared *asada* are grilled, which is a nonfat cooking process. *Fajitas* are made up of grilled meat or chicken, and then rolled into a soft (non-fried) tortilla. Seafood served 'Veracruz style' is baked in a tomato sauce, and *chile verde* is pork simmered with vegetables and green chillies. *Salsa* is made with tomato, onion, chillies and herbs – virtually fat-free and bursting with vitamins A and C. The soups on most Mexican menus are relatively healthy. Try starting off with *gazpacho* or black bean and vegetable soup.

Frijoles are refried beans, a purple mush served with virtually everything. They are usually cooked in lard and then mixed with cheese, making them very high in fat. If your Spanish is up to it, ask for whole, non-refried beans instead. Use *salsa* on your main course, instead of sour cream and cheese, or ask for reduced-fat sour cream. An intriguing dish is *Mole Poblano*, Mexico's national speciality with turkey or chicken and a sauce made from chocolate, chillies and many spices.Portions tend to be on the large size, so beware anything that is described as 'large'. Mexican desserts are limited but you can always have excellent fruit such as mango, guava and papaya, all of which are far less calorific than *sopapillas* (deep-fried sweet pastries) or fried ice cream, which are the usual (and death defying) alternatives. However a usually safe street food is a *tamale*, packets of corn dough wrapped in corn husks or banana leaves.

Be particularly careful if buying food from street vendors. They are usually very poor with minimal cooking facilities, and hygiene is not top of their list of priorities.

South America

The South American continent is vast and varied and it is difficult to summarise briefly the variety of cooking you will find there. However, here's a whirlwind tour.

The cuisine of South America stems from a combination of diverse cultural influences and the available produce. You'll find lots of local dishes, but you'll also find international dishes and the ubiquitous fast food outlets. In general, South American food is reasonably low in fat, although in Argentina in particular you are likely to eat rather more meat than may be good for you – particularly as portions tend to be huge. The biggest danger, though, is the drinking water – in several South American countries, it is none too pure and ice made with polluted water is not at all uncommon.

Argentina

Argentine cuisine is influenced by waves of European immigration, particularly from Italy. You'll find many Italian restaurants and pizzerias, plus *heladerias*, or ice-cream parlours, serving Italian cuisine and *gelatos*. Argentina is known for its beef, and many meals are based on substantial amounts of the stuff.

Popular dishes include *asado* which consists of various cuts of meat cooked over coals and usually served with *chimichurri* marinade, french fries and salad; *parillada carbonada*, a beef stew with rice, potatoes, sweet potatoes, corn, squash, apples and pears; *puchero*, a casserole made with beef, chicken, bacon, sausage, corn, peppers, tomatoes, onions, cabbage, sweet potatoes and squash; roasted suckling pig; *noquis* which consists of gnocchi or potato dumplings served with tomato sauce; a*rroz con pollo*, a chicken and rice casserole with eggs and vegetables; *locro*, corn, white beans, beef, sausage and squash in a stew; and *empanada de humita* which are pasties filled with corn, onion, cheese and flour.

Chile

Chilean cuisine tends to the international, with excellent seafood forming the basis of many popular dishes. Ethnic restaurants abound in the cities and vegetarian meals are widely available.

Popular dishes include *cazuela* which is soup with meat or chicken, potato, corn and squash or other vegetables; *pastel de choclo* which is a pie with meat, vegetables, chicken, olives and hard-boiled eggs; *lomo a lo pobre*, steak, eggs, onions and french fries; *arroz con pollo*, a chicken and rice casserole; *currant*, a seafood stew with chicken, pork, lamb, beef and potato; and *chupes* which is a stew of fish or beef.

Ecuador

Tropical fruits and seafood are popular and plentiful, particularly from markets. Various soups are often drunk for breakfast in local markets. A popular dish consists of steak, fried eggs, vegetables, fried potatoes, avocado, rice and tomato. Other things to try include *cuy* which is grilled guinea pig; *lechón*: roasted suckling pig; *llapingachos*: potato and cheese pancake, often served with small bits of meat; *tortillas de maiz*: corn pancakes; *locro*: soup with potatoes, corn and avocado; *parrilla*: barbecued mixed meat; *tortillas de maiz*: corn pancakes, and *yaguarlocro locro* which is made with blood sausage and I am told is a truly acquired taste!

Brazil

This huge country offers a cuisine as diverse as its regions and climates, with the staples being rice and beans. *Manioc* (made from the root of cassava) is used as flour and a seasoning. Many dishes show their African roots. Fruits are many and varied, some found only in Brazil.

Popular dishes include *carne de sol:* grilled salted meat served with beans, rice and vegetables; *caruru*: a mixture of okra, shrimp, vegetables and peppers made into a sauce for fish; *cozido*: a vegetable stew; *feijoada*: meat stew served with rice and beans; *mocueca*: a stew-like seafood sauce made with coconut milk and cooked in a clay pot; *pato no tucupi*: roast duck with *tucupi* sauce made from manioc and vegetables; *peixe a delícia*: boiled or grilled fish served with bananas and coconut milk*; procure ao forno:* Amazon river fish baked with lemon and seasonings; *tutu á mineira*: bean, bacon and manioc sauce served with cabbage and *vatapá*: seafood served with a manioc and coconut sauce.

Paraguay and Uruguay

Guarani are the indigenous inhabitants of Paraguay and their cooking styles and names are reflected in the Paraguayan diet. Fruit, vegetables and meat are consumed along with manioc and corn.

When in Paraguay, be sure to try *parrillada* which consists of various types of meat cooked over coals, as in Argentina. Other popular dishes include *mazamorroa* which is a sort of corn mush; *sopa paraguaya*: corn bread with cheese and onion; *mbaipy-so-ó*: corn pudding with chunks of meat; *bori-bori*: chicken soup with cornmeal dumplings *Sooyo sopy*: soup with ground meat, served with rice or noodles; *chipa soo:* corn bread with a meat filling; and *chipa*: manioc bread with egg and cheese.

A popular desert is *mbaipy-he-é* which consists of corn, milk and molasses.

Uruguay reflects European traditions in some of its cuisine, as well as influences from neighbouring countries.

Staple dishes include *parrilla:* grilled meats, Argentine style; *puchero:* beef, vegetables, chicken, bacon, beans and sausages; *chivito:* steak sandwich with lettuce, bacon, tomato cheese or a larger version called *chivito al plato Olympicos. Cazuela* is soup made with either seafood or tripe.

Uruguayan desserts come recommended but none, it has to be said, are heart friendly.

Columbia

I have never been to Columbia, but if you find yourself there, I am told that the things to go for are *ajiaco:* chicken soup with potatoes, corn and capers; and *bandeja paisa:* ground beef, chorizo, beans, fried banana, fried egg; and *chicarrón.* I wasn't sure what *chicarrón* was in English so I got Google to translate a recipe on a Spanish website. For your edification, key ingredients include '*three dangerous eggs, 250 grams of worn out bread, salt and pepper to the pleasure.*'

Other pleasures include *cuy:* grilled guinea pig; *hormiga culona:* fried ants (yes ANTS); *lechona:* baked pig stuffed with meat, rice, peas and *tamales:* pork, rice and vegetables mix, steamed in banana leaves, which is also a popular street food in Mexico, though they are normally filled with corn meal.

Venezuela

Venezuelan specialities include *arepas:* flat bread, either served plain at meals or filled with meat; cheese, or fish and eaten as a snack; fresh corn pancake, like a *tortilla*, served with cheese and/or ham; *cachito:* hot bread roll stuffed with ham; *hallaca:* meat, vegetables, olive stuffing in corn dough, steamed in plantain leaves; *mondongo:* tripe cooked in broth with vegetables, corn and potatoes; *muchacho:* roast loin of beef in sauce; *pabellón:* shredded beef, rice, beans and fried plantain; *parillada:* barbequed meats and *sancocho:* fish stew with vegetables.

Guyana

Guyana's cuisine shows definite ethnic influences from the East Indies, China and Creole cooking. Popular dishes include spicy pepperpot stew; rice; curries; cowheel soup (memories of Desperate Dan for those of you old enough to remember the *Beano*), and seafood dishes.

Asia

China

Although a lot of tourists to China complain about lousy food, I think this is due to the fact that most travel in groups, and are the victims of mass catering. The Chinese diet is reasonably heart-friendly with plenty of vegetables, seafood and soy beans. Sugar, dairy products and meat are used very sparingly, and most meals are based on fresh ingredients, and are mainly baked or stir-fried. However deep fried food has its place, too, particularly as a starter. You may want to go easy on (fried) *crab rangoon, wontons* and some egg or spring rolls. Instead, try steamed egg or spring rolls, beef teriyaki, or clear broth soups. Order steamed white rice or plain noodles instead of the fried versions. Choose dishes that are steamed or baked rather than fried or sautéed.

It is important to understand that authentic Chinese food bears little relationship to the Westernised meals we are used to. Sweet and sour pork and chicken balls are more often found in Balham than Beijing.

Chinese cuisine varies from region to region. *Cantonese* food in southern China emphasises pork, chicken and dumplings. *Szechuan* is found in inland China and is noted for its hot, spicy seasonings, with many high-fat dishes fried in oil. Food from the northern region of Beijing (Peking) features duck and noodles while Shanghai, on the coast, is known for seafood. *Mandarin* cooking refers to aristocratic cuisine, highlighting the best of regional cooking.

A warning: Chinese food is often high in salt. Oyster, black bean and soy sauces are major sources of sodium, as is monosodium glutamate (MSG).

India

The basic ingredients of Indian food are grains, vegetables, beans and meat or fish mixed with yoghurt. Typical dishes contain lentils, chickpeas, rice, beans and spices such as cardamom, cinnamon and cloves.

However, plenty of fat is added during food preparation. Many dishes are cooked in *ghee* (clarified butter), which can raise the proportion of calories from fat to almost 50%. Other dishes are made with coconut oil, which contains almost all saturated fat.

Most restaurant curries are made with coconut milk, although you may be able to order a yoghurt-based version. If you have the courage or someone to interpret for you, always ask the waiter how food is prepared. Items that include the words *kandhari, malai* or *korma* indicate dishes high in cream or coconut milk.

Among the healthier options are *pulkas, nan, chapati* and *kulcha* (various types of baked, low-fat breads); salad or vegetables with yoghurt dressing; *mulligatawny* (chicken) or *del rasam* (lentil) soups; chicken and fish cooked *tandoori* (marinated and baked) or *vindoori-style* (marinated and braised).

The danger zones include *samosa* (fried meat or vegetables); *pakori* (deep-fried breads and vegetables); and thick cheese puddings and honeyed pastries. Instead, opt for *khur*, a sweetened rice pudding, or fruit chutney. Also you need to be careful where you eat – *Delhi Belly* is all too common among visitors to India and can seriously knock you for six.

South Indian cuisine, which is largely vegetarian, has a greater emphasis on rice than in the North and uses coconut and curry leaves liberally.

Japan

I am not a great fan of Japanese food, but you can't ignore the fact that the country has one of the lowest obesity rates in the world. The Japanese associate eating with healing and they eat foods that take care of their bodies. Their diet consists largely of vegetables, fresh fish, soy products and green tea, with little meat, sugar or processed foods.

I recently visited Japan for the first time and was taken to a very upmarket restaurant by some young friends – an IT whiz-kid from Glasgow and his wife, who is one of Japan's foremost flamenco dancers (yes, really). Although the meal was slightly strange with very unfamiliar tastes and textures, it did wonders for my usually dodgy digestive system and I felt really well the next day.

The Japanese believe in the benefits of cruciferous vegetables such as cabbage, broccoli, cauliflower, radishes, kale, Brussels sprouts and turnips, which contain high levels of glucosinolates, which are believed by many Japanese to fight certain types of cancer, including those of the lung and colon. However anyone on anti-blood clotting agents such as warfarin should go easy on these as they can speed clotting.

Another primary ingredient in the Japanese is *miso* (a fermented soy product). If you're watching your sodium intake, pass on the very popular *miso* soup and the salted, smoked or pickled fish, as all contain a lot of salt. Having said that, *miso* has been shown to lower cholesterol and cure intestinal problems.

Seaweed and green tea are also popular. Green tea is rich in antioxidants, which can fight infection. It has also been associated with lowered blood pressure. Best for you is Japan's most famous food – *sushi*. Whether fish is cooked or raw, it has high doses of omega-3 fatty acids and lean protein.

Tempura, *agemono* and *katsu* refer to foods that are breaded and fried. You can control your fat intake by ordering foods that are *yaki* (broiled or grilled) or *nimono* (simmered). For example, beef *teriyaki* is marinated in soy sauce and rice wine and then grilled. Chicken *yakitori* is skewered, then grilled or broiled. You should remember, however, that *soy* and *teriyaki* sauces are also fairly high in sodium.

As an alternative, ask for dishes prepared without *soy* sauce or request low-sodium *soy* sauce – although this may be impossible as you probably won't be able to speak Japanese and the waiter is unlikely to speak English. For flavour without sodium, use a tiny bit of shredded *wasabi*, a very strong horseradish.

Thailand

Thai food is usually heart-friendly and very fresh. The fact that you rarely see an overweight Thai is witness to the fact that the local cuisine in general is low in fat and carbohydrates and full of fruit and vegetables – just as the heart doctor ordered!

This is a country of 24-hour eating. On the street there is food of all varieties at all time of the day and night, ranging from fresh fruits including mangoes, Thai oranges, apples, strawberries and various exotic fruits which you may not even recognise, to *kanom krok* (coconut rice pancakes) which are mainly available in the morning.

Trays of prepared foods such as curries, basil pork and Chinese broccoli with oyster sauce are also on offer as well as grilled sour sausage, sticky rice and *haw moek,* which is a fish curry mousse.

Make sure the vendor and equipment look clean, the ingredients look fresh and then eat only food that is still warm from cooking or that you saw cooked right in front of you. Like everywhere else, be cautious about eating unpeeled fruit and veg. Unfortunately from a health point of view, western junk food can now be found everywhere and they are beginning to nudge out the traditional Thai food stalls.

There are also a lot of non-Thai restaurants – Italian, French, Japanese and Indian – although the result tends to be somewhat of a hybrid. Japanese restaurants proliferate and are possibly a safe low-fat bet.

Most traditional Thai restaurants fall into one of two categories: stand-alone restaurants and shop front restaurants. The stand-alone restaurants are more or less conventional while the shop front variety are often family-run. They usually have some sort of food display out front so you can see how fresh things are and select seafood to be cooked. They may be noodle shops, in which case they'll have noodles displayed along with the type of meat that goes in the noodle. Décor is usually minimal or non-existent.

Typical dishes in these shops include *yum bplah krawb* (dried crispy fish salad) and *boong fai daeng* (stir-fried morning glory with chillies and fish steamed with Chinese celery and sour plum).

The more expensive conventional Thai restaurants will often feature seafood but meals can be surprisingly dull. Thais have a proclivity to want people to be happy. In many places, particularly in tourist areas, restaurants have had experiences with westerners who could not eat spicy food, so they make their cuisine quite bland. It is worth learning a few Thai phrases so that you can tell them that you want it prepared 'Thai style' and that you are able to eat spicy food – that is assuming that you don't like bland food.

One of the more bizarre (but highly recommended) restaurants in Bangkok is a place called the *Cabbage and Condom,* which as its name implies, is improbably run by a sexual health project.

Vietnam
Vietnam is great for delicate hearts provided you like your food spicy. The country has three basic regional cuisines. North Vietnamese food is not quite as rich or spicy as that of the country's south and is quite

subtle, using black pepper rather than red chillies. The food of the North looks and tastes much more like Chinese food than that found in other parts of the country.

The hottest food in the country is from Central Vietnam. Chilli peppers are found everywhere and in everything.

In Vietnam's southern region, vegetables predominate. While vegetables are as likely as not to be pickled in Hanoi, they will be fresh in Saigon. The cuisine of Vietnam's southern region is also more influenced by the French colonial era. You will always smell baguettes baking in Saigon and southern Vietnamese prefer to serve several small dishes at mealtime, instead of two or three large helpings.

There are a few basic staple dishes. One is *pho* — or beef noodle soup. *Pho* is the fast food of Saigon, Hanoi, Danang, Hue and Haiphong. Almost anywhere you go you will also find *gio lua* (pork sausages), *nem ran* (spring rolls) and *cha ca* (fish balls). And seafood is abundant – crabs, shrimp, squids, mussels, and a huge variety of fish and lobster, fished in the waters off Vietnam's coast or from the country's rivers. You will also find *nouc mam* (fish sauce) on almost any table where the Chinese would place *soy* sauce.

Finally, no meal is complete without a tray of herbs and fresh vegetables. Almost anywhere in the country you will find sliced cucumbers, hot peppers, coriander, bean threads, basil and mint. While beef, chicken, pork and shrimps are standard fare, you may encounter snake or dog meat – cause for another heart attack, I fear.

Australasia
Australia
When I first visited Australia twenty years ago, the food was gruesome but familiar from inedible school meals. Meat and three veg (cooked virtually to extinction) were the order of the day, but this has changed radically with the influx of immigrants, particularly from places such as Vietnam.

Aussie cuisine is now as diverse and often as sophisticated as any else in the world. Modern Australian cuisine draws from its South East Asian neighbours, as well as by the many waves of immigrants from Greece, Lebanon and Italy.

This is good news for low-fat food seekers. Fresh produce is readily available and the government has done a lot to encourage low-salt, low-fat, healthy cookery, incorporating lean meat and lightly cooked, steamed or stir-fried vegetables.

Australia also has a wide variety of seafood and the iconic 'barbies' are great for healthy eating, although sausages and onion served on white bread with tomato sauce are not unheard of. Some English trends are still evident in domestic cuisine, among them a widespread tradition of having a hot roast turkey, chicken and/or ham with all the trimmings for Christmas dinner, followed by Christmas pudding. It can seem quite odd eating Christmas dinner in the blazing sunshine of an Australian summer's day!

However not everything is healthy. There are plenty of ghastly fat-filled takeaways to match the British high street at its worst. Meat pies and sausage rolls are still favourites and large queues line up outside Sydney's iconic *Harry's Cafe de Wheels* in Woolamaloo for meat pie and mash which, frankly, is not much to write home about.

Chinese and Asian restaurants are usually better than their UK counterparts and the food malls that you find in every town and city offer very good quality low-fat meals with loads of fresh vegetables and fruit at pretty low prices. So Oz is definitely a winner for the heart. However, do let yourself off bounds at least once to try *Lamingtons* and *Anzac* biscuits. *Lamingtons* are basically sponge cakes with jam and coconut, while *Anzacs* are, well, utterly delicious. I am sure your heart will forgive you this little indulgence.

New Zealand

On a recent trip to New Zealand, I found eating out a fairly uninspiring experience but perfectly all right if you were heart-watching. A survey by **Tourism New Zealand** found that 'there was some dissatisfaction in terms of delivering unique eating out/restaurant experiences, although this aspect is not overly important in driving activity satisfaction'. Roughly translated this means that the food is perfectly adequate but hardly worth travelling across the world for. The survey also found that visitors from the USA and UK were more satisfied with their eating out and restaurant experiences than those from Canada, Germany or Asia – enough said.

The survey also highlighted that visitors complained about the lack of specific New Zealand dishes and that, while the quality of restaurant meals was certainly adequate, they were nothing special and not considered particularly good value for money. There were also complaints that restaurant were often closed on public holidays and had limited opening hours.

Having said that, New Zealand cuisine is generally fresh and quite diverse. Because of the Pacific Rim influence, it is perfectly easy to eat healthily, and there are plenty of fresh fruit and veg wherever you go.

For dishes that have a distinctly New Zealand style, there's lamb, pork, venison, salmon, lobster, oysters, mussels, scallops and *pipis* and *tustus* which are both local shellfish. New Zealand lamb is of course famous throughout the world and you do see an awful lot of sheep on your travels through the North and South islands.

The New Zealand summer sees a lot of barbecues. A Maori speciality is the *hangi* (pronounced hung-ee), a pit in which meats or fish are cooked with vegetables. A deep hole is dug in the ground, lined with red-hot stones and covered with vegetation. The food is then placed on top. The whole oven is sprinkled with water and sealed with more vegetation. The hole is then filled with earth and left to steam for several hours. Traditionally, men dig and prepare the hole, and women prepare the food to go in it. All members of an extended family (*whanau*) help out.

Hangis are a major attraction for tourists and you often see them advertised, usually accompanied by a demonstration of Maori culture and dancing.

For the homesick, fish and chips (out of bounds for most heart sufferers) are available everywhere and are as variable as their UK counterparts. A favourite pud is *pavlova,* a fruit and meringue concoction named after the ballerina, Anna Pavlova. The aforementioned *Lamingtons* and *Anzac* biscuits are also, thankfully, in evidence.

Chapter 5

Walk the Walk

Seeing the World on Foot

If you would grow great and stately,
You must try to walk sedately
R L Stevenson, *A Child's Garden of Verses*

The last thing I was told by the cardiologist as I left hospital was to make sure that I walked as much as possible and to step out briskly in order to stimulate my heart. For the first few weeks after I got home, a gentle amble to the local shops was as much as I could cope with, but little by little I became a little more adventurous.

However, I must admit that I am still not a terribly enthusiastic walker, unless the terrain is fairly level and the route well defined. But a walking holiday – as opposed to ambling round your local park – is an excellent and often low-cost way of seeing the countryside both here and abroad.

First for some walking facts which should get you out of your armchair and on to the footpath:

- Sedentary lifestyle is one of the 10 leading global causes of death and disability. More than 2,000,000 deaths world-wide each year are attributable to physical inactivity. (**World Health Organisation**, *Move for Health*, 2002)
- Regular walking reduces the risk of coronary heart disease by up to 50%. (**Department of Health**)
- Lack of exercise causes more illness than smoking in EU countries. (**World Health Organisation**, 2002)
- A brisk one-mile walk in 20 minutes burns around 100

calories – as much as swimming for 10 minutes, playing football for 12 minutes or doing aerobics for 16 minutes.

- Car users regularly suffer up to three times as much pollution as pedestrians because they are sitting in traffic in the line of exhaust fumes from the car in front. (**Environmental Transport Association**)
- An increase in walking pace from three to four miles per hour can lead to a doubling of improvement in fitness.
- Even 10-minute brisk walks can increase fitness.

Worried? Well it's never too late to do something about it. If you are not a seasoned walker, one of the best organisations to consult is the **Ramblers Association** (RA) (*www.ramblers.org.uk*), although many local authorities run walking programmes as part of their keep fit efforts.

The RA's research shows walking for as little as 30 minutes a day can help prevent heart disease and stroke, strengthen the bones and improves flexibility and co-ordination. Moreover, in a recent poll, two-thirds of people said walking helped them with stress, depression, anxiety and problem-solving.

The right walking speed for you depends on your gender, age and fitness. The table below shows target speeds for people who want to be fit. For example, if you are a woman aged 57 who can walk briskly at a speed of 3 miles per hour, then you are fit.

These speeds are based on flat ground. If there are gradients on your walk then increase the time by between 10% and 20%.

The goal of taking 10,000 steps a day has been widely promoted and has led to the use of pedometers to count steps. Two new Australian studies report the characteristics of people who do, or do not, achieve that goal.

Walking speed mph, Walking briskly and slightly out of breath						
MEN	WOMEN	AGE UP TO 39 YRS	AGE 40-54 YRS	AGE 55-64 YRS	AGE 65-74 YRS	AGE 75 AND OVER
5.0	4.5	Fit	Very fit	Very fit	Very fit	Wow
4.5	4.0	Fit	Fit	Very fit	Very fit	Very fit
4.0	3.5	Fit	Fit	Very fit	Very fit	Very fit
3.5	3.0	Unfit	Just Fit	Fit	Fit	Fit
3.0	2.5	Unfit	Unfit	Just fit	Just fit	Fit
2.5	2.0	Unfit	Unfit	Unfit	Just fit	Just fit

In Australia, 428 people wore a pedometer and provided a record of steps for four or more days of one week. On average men reported significantly more steps than women. Men who were more likely to report 10,000 or more steps per day regularly walked in the workplace, did vigorous activity at work or were employed in a blue-collar occupation. Men who did not achieve the goal were likely to be 60 years of age or older and overweight. Women who reached 10,000 steps a day reported 150 minutes or more of leisure-time physical activity, and those who did not were overweight.

The first bit of advice you will receive is not to overdo it, particularly if you have a heart condition. **The Ramblers' Association** says that there is no reason why you have to walk a long-distance path from end to end in one go. Though many people enjoy the sense of achievement in doing this, it is probably not the best approach for those new to long-distance walking. Many paths, particularly those in more populated areas, can be approached flexibly, and as a series of day walks between points connected by frequent public transport.

Alternatively, you can complete a path over a number of weekend or longer breaks: some people have even walked from Lands End to John O'Groats this way over the course of several years. You can also use a long distance path as the basis of a circular walk, completing the circle using other footpaths. Some paths even have marked circular alternatives along the route.

The RA strongly recommends that if you are new to long-distance walking, it's advisable to practise before embarking on a longer route. You should try a series of day walks, doing the same sort of distance you'll be walking over your intended route, over similar terrain and carrying a similar load.

My brother-in-law, John Robinson, is an inveterate walker and has made some very helpful observations.

He stresses that walking gives you an appetite (and a thirst) and aids digestion. It is relatively cheap and if you pick your spots, perhaps you'll see something interesting – animals, birds, trees, flowers – which change with the seasons. "You can walk the same route more than once without getting bored because it changes over the months" he points out. "Perhaps there'll be a good view to enjoy. So do the walk again or in reverse because it then looks different. Get off-road and see things/places you wouldn't normally visit and, unless going to some popular and accessible spot, get away from people. At a walking pace you see things that the motorist doesn't. After all, when you walk you can go at your own pace."

He advises that you should choose your routes by whatever criteria take your fancy: long/short, uphill/downhill, high/low, hills/valleys, rivers/woods/meadows, challenging/easy, circular/linear, etc. The great aids are the *OS 1:25000 Explorer and Outdoor Leisure* series of maps. These are purely depictive but to a high level of detail, including field boundaries. Though not infallible or always up-to-date, they are invaluable for choosing a route and then navigating it.

He points out, though, that they are big and unmanageable in wind or rain, so suggests pre-folding the map and buying a map case to put it in. There are also numerous guides readily available, whether for particular areas or themes, e.g. pub walks, walking with children, etc. These are usually in book form and so are more manageable than map. However unless OS-based, their plans tend to be sketchy and vary from wholly adequate to useless. What they mostly do have, is some written commentary to provide directions and often useful information about what you might see or do en route.

John – who is a retired senior planning officer – stresses that by law, all footpaths should be signed at the point where they leave/join a metalled highway. This isn't always the case, which is odd, as signing is one of a council's audit commission targets, and they get easy points for providing them.

Many paths are marked along the route, particularly at junctions with other routes. This can be very useful, but is not usually a substitute for a map, partly because one comes to rely on it and if it's missing or inconsistent, you might not know where you are.

John says: 'In my experience, there's little use for a compass, unless in open country and on a longish route where there are no particular landmarks. On high moors, or up in the mountains, then positional accuracy can be vital to the point that it's probably better to have a GPS. As there are now an increasing number of right-to-roam areas, which almost by definition don't have many tracks, some directional device may be very useful.'

Most of the perils of walking in England should be well known, but anybody planning a walk should bear in mind:

1. Popularity

While most people don't go far from their cars, there are some walks which have become too popular – for instance Ingelborough in North Yorkshire – and have become seriously eroded. The response has often been to pave the paths (at vast expense), which diminishes their appeal. So, if you want a 'natural' walk, stay away from these major routes. There are also locations which, because of ease of access, shortness of route and appeal, attract a lot of people. Malham Cove, again in North Yorkshire, for example, is rightly classed as worth a visit, but you will see it with a lot of others.

2. Animals

Bullocks are curious and will charge towards and follow you but are not generally harmful. There are a few cases each year of people getting trampled by cattle, usually, it seems, when a cow feels her calf is being threatened. You should also be wary of bulls. Horses can be friendly but some may harass you. Geese can be offensive. Make sure any dog is under control.

3. Unrestored and overgrown paths

Paths are supposed by law to be restored after ploughing/planting. This rule is frequently ignored and the council may not always wish to act if the crop is established. Some farmers also plough too close to the field edge, leaving an inadequate margin. Often the margin is overgrown leaving no choice but to walk in the field. Plant growth can be amazing and a path can be covered in vegetation in a few weeks. The worst seasonal problems are nettles, brambles and briars, but over a longer period, blackthorn and hawthorn can be a real nuisance. There seems to be no drive to keep paths clear, but some parish councils, local groups and/or individuals make real efforts.

4. Stiles

There is scope for a book on the diversity of these, which can be vertical or horizontal or both. The former vary greatly from the two-step type in southern England to the tall ladder styles of the Yorkshire Dales. There are kissing gates, barrel styles, creeps through walls, etc. What they mostly have in common is that they are not pedestrian-friendly. They are either too high, in poor repair, offer inadequate foot support or are overgrown and some even are topped by barbed wire. They are not infrequently placed where cattle stand, and are only accessible by paddling through mud. Many are historic in that they originally served to give access through a field, but didn't allow cattle to escape. With the vast reduction in stock-keeping, many of these now have no purpose but they keep on being installed.

5. Diversions

Though there is a legal presumption to keep paths as they are, they can be diverted or even closed for some reasons. In some cases you might cynically wonder whether the real reason was to make a property more valuable. This is a continual process and the actual path may differ from the map. Hopefully any changes should be adequately signed, but there will always be cases where there's no indication.

6. Difficult/dangerous paths

There are plenty of these. In particular, watch out for any path that comes to a main road/motorway and consider what you are going to do when you get there. Many paths start from/finish on major roads. You may find that you have been left high and dry with nowhere to go, as very few will have a footway or even a passable verge so that you can get to the next path in reasonable safety. Always plan some alternative route.

7. Rubbish

Alarming amounts of rubbish are tipped, often in places where you might wonder how it was worth anyone's while to drive to so isolated a spot. A widespread phenomenon is the burnt-out car.

8. Off-roaders

You will encounter bikes, motorbikes and 4x4s more often than you might expect. Frequently they shouldn't be there, but they are entitled by law to use byways, etc. Apart from conflict with pedestrians and horse-riders, they can't half make a mess of a track but, then, that is exactly why they do it. Fortunately, there are moves afoot to reduce their use. Horses can also be a nuisance since they can chew up tracks too in busy areas.

John is a bit of a cynic and is not easily led by fashion or style – he still wears his wedding suit on formal occasions, despite the fact that he has just celebrated his fortieth wedding anniversary! Hence his view that the walkers one often sees with all the right gear, tend to be poseurs. He argues that you can spend a fortune on the 'right' clothing and equipment. This is all right for serious, all-weather, go-anywhere-anytime walkers. However he suspects that, often, it's all a bit of show and that it is appearance rather than substance, that's important to the walker.

He does emphasise the importance of good footwear, nonetheless. You need comfort, support, stability and some degree of protection from the elements. Ordinary shoes might be all right for a walk round the park, but going off-road perhaps needs more consideration. If the walk is reasonably smooth going and dry, then a pair of trainers is often adequate. However if you are walking along stony, rutted, muddy and overgrown paths, something more rugged is sensible. He normally walks either in boots or heavy-duty, cross-country trainers, depending on the weather, ground conditions and route. Boots can be very expensive and such cost may be difficult to justify for the casual walker.

There are boots, like the Hi-Tech range, which are more moderately priced, and while these may lack the sophistication and, indeed, the weather-resistant qualities of the more expensive boots, they are quite adequate for lighter use.

If you are you going out in wet weather or in the cold, a good jacket is needed – ideally waterproof and windproof, while wearing several layers of clothing helps you to keep warm. If cold, wear gloves and a woolly hat, or use the hood of your jacket; if wet, wear some waterproof headgear and waterproof pants too.

There are clothes made of special materials which may be water/cold resistant and/or quick-drying. Once again, these can start costing serious money, which may be excessive for limited or casual use. Gaiters are cheap enough though, and do help to keep your feet and lower legs dry. Taking a hot drink could be advisable, so this means a flask.

Even in the UK, you might go out in the sun. There are shirts, trousers, etc., which are proofed to protect against ultraviolet rays.

But for many, sensible dress should be sufficient. A sun hat may be a good idea as well as a water bottle.

All this gear needs a rucksack. Once again, there is a vast range available. John warns, though, that you've got to carry the damn thing, so don't get one that's too big and make sure it is going to be comfortable on your shoulders. Many people also find a stick helpful. The traditional walking stick is useful enough, but there are various types of walking pole which are usually adjustable and may have other features. Prices have come down and you can buy them for less than £10.

Geoff Watkins is one of those walkers who prefers his own company when he is out hiking. He maintains that solitary walking undoubtedly has its own appeal. He told me that you do not need to go as far as the celebrated walker Alfred Wainwright, who argued that one only ever walks alone, anything else being conversation on the move. Here is his advice.

"Anyone is capable of managing walks on their own. For those who have no ambition to devise their own walks using map and compass, there are more than enough published guides to keep you going for a lifetime. It is also worth remembering that no walk is ever the same twice, so don't be put off from repeating familiar routes.

Sensible safety precautions that apply to all walking are even more crucial if you are setting off alone. Lone walkers are advised to carry waterproofs at all times and always to check the likely weather conditions, especially if going anywhere at all remote. Most of the United Kingdom is perfectly suitable for walking in the rain, provided you are appropriately clad and shod. There is no need to be just a fair-weather walker, and a willingness to walk when the sun is not shining extends your opportunities for exercise throughout the year.

Mobile phones provide great comfort but you should remember that there is not always network coverage, particularly in more remote areas like the North Pennines. Therefore it is always a good idea to make sure someone knows where you have gone in case of emergency.

The need for precautions should not be off-putting to any would-be walker. After a while, they just become second nature. On the positive side walking alone has a number of attractions. One of the most relaxing aspects is that you can always go at your own pace, without worrying whether you might be holding a companion up, or indeed forging ahead too fast for them. You can also stop exactly when and where you please. To some, this may sound rather selfish, but if it is your well-being which is at stake, there is nothing wrong with that on occasions. After all, nobody spends their entire life on solitary walks – there is plenty of time left for other things and other people.

It is also a good opportunity to develop interests linked to your walking, while not subjecting other people to your own particular enthusiasm. Several walkers are also keen photographers, and the opportunities for spotting the minute, the transitory, the half-hidden and at times the downright quirky, make for a fascinating range of subject matter. For others, it is the opportunity to study nature at close quarters that adds to the appeal.

The range of plants in any stretch of countryside is quite astonishing, and the chance to view wildlife at close quarters can be a source of positive excitement; mammals may often be difficult to spot, apart from the ubiquitous rabbits, but there is usually a wealth of fascinating birdlife, not to mention insects.

Perhaps the greatest appeal of solitary walking is the opportunity it provides for clear thinking. Much of the time, the walking is not particularly demanding in terms of physical effort or concentration, though obviously there are exceptions when the terrain or route-finding demand your full attention and effort. When you are striding along a clear path, there is a great sense of your head being clear, too – clear simply to soak up the world around you or to come afresh at something that needs thinking through."

Those over whom solitary walking exerts no appeal, often ask Geoff whether he gets bored with his own company. He admits that this might be a particular issue if you were contemplating setting off alone on a long-distance walk and acknowledges that it is certainly a very different prospect from a half-day, or even day-long, walk. However it can be enormously rewarding and not necessarily as lonely as might be thought. Again, you don't have to plunge with trepidation into the 'big ones' such as the Pennine Way, which is by no means everyone's cup of tea, as there are now an enormous number of 'Ways' of varying length and difficulty, both in Britain and elsewhere.

You can always start with something fairly straightforward, and graduate to the bigger challenges as you gain in confidence. There is enormous satisfaction in setting off with a goal in view and then, some days later, attaining that goal. This is probably why many walkers prefer the linear routes, though circular routes can be attractive as well, and they often have the advantage of being easier to organise in terms of transport.

Whether you opt for a linear or a circular long-distance walk, a big decision is whether to stay in B&Bs or to be a true back-packer with your own tent. Whilst camping does give you more scope as to where to break your journey, this is really only for the adventurous or young and, if you are walking alone, for the exceptionally self-sufficient. For most walkers, part of the pleasure of a long-distance walk is to be able, after a long and satisfying, but tiring, day on the trail, to experience the comfort of a bed and bath or shower; and the evening meal in the farmhouse, or the drink in the local pub.

This is the time to chat with locals or share experiences with fellow-walkers – the social side of walking. You may well have already met some of your fellow-walkers in the pub earlier in the day, for unless you really are tackling the remote wildernesses – and there are only a handful left in this country – you will be constantly encountering others who are enjoying the experience as much as you are. These encounters remind you that the solitude you have experienced for much of the day is what you have chosen for a while, and is all the sweeter for it.

The Ramblers' Association is keen to emphasise that you should take time to eat and enjoy the scenery – walking does not need to be an endurance test. You will obviously need to stop for meal breaks and rests, but you will also want to take your time to enjoy other features along the route: remember to allow for looking around interesting towns and villages and visiting attractions like historic buildings, museums, nature reserves, and so on, if you are likely to want to do so.

The RA reminds walkers to account for other factors that will increase the walking time. Walking uphill takes more time; a walker's rule of thumb is to add 30 minutes for every 300m of height gained. Muddy, sandy, ploughed or otherwise difficult paths will slow you down, as will navigational mistakes, and even with waterproofs, you

> Most long-distance walkers probably travel somewhere between 10 and 20 miles a day along relatively flat and easy paths, though there is no reason why you shouldn't do less, and some determined walkers do more. As you do more walking, you will become more sure of your preferences and the extent of your abilities.

may still prefer to take shelter for a while rather than walk in the rain. And though paths along popular and widely promoted long-distance routes are less likely to be blocked, you may still encounter problems of this kind. Always allow for delays, and, when in doubt, over-estimate rather than under-estimate the time it will take you to complete a section of route, especially when you have to register at your accommodation or catch a bus or train.

It is always best to plan and book your accommodation well in advance, especially if you intend to walk a well-known and popular route during the summer months. The RA website (*www.ramblers.org*) has useful accommodation listings and links from the individual path pages as well as information on transport links and tourist information centres.

Youth hostels (oldies can stay at them too, though you may feel outnumbered) can be found on or near some of the paths, but very few routes can be walked throughout using youth hostels alone. On some paths, one-stop-shop booking services for youth hostels are available. However I did promise that this book would not be too harsh on you, so you will find, at the end of this book, a list of decent hotels in good walking country.

Furthermore, because you simply may not feel like organising your own walking tour, we have also listed the many, mostly small and personally run companies, that specialise in walking holidays and do all the hard work (apart from the actual walking) for you.

Another extremely useful web site is *www.go4awalk.com* which offers a wealth of information on just about every aspect of walking – not least where to go. It provides details of hundreds of UK walks in PDF format, and there are competitions, forums for sharing experiences, a photographic gallery and lots of hints and tips for getting the most out of walking in the UK.

Here are some examples – some of them vaguely disgusting but undoubtedly useful – that I found on the web site:

- Remember to have some dry warm clothes waiting in your car to change into after long walk.
- If you suffer from back problems that are made worse when walking with a rucksack (and not to have one would mean going without food and water for the day!) – always use a properly fitting one that has a good padded waistband.
- Turkey-sized roasting bags, available from supermarkets, are light and much, much tougher than ordinary plastic bags. They are good for keeping gear dry in your rucksack and make very good map cases.
- Keep a 35mm film canister full of surgical spirit in your first aid kit, along with a needle threaded with cotton (not nylon). If you get a really big blister, soak the needle and thread in the cotton, then pass them through the blister and squeeze.
- Newly formed unbroken blisters can be treated by applying Bonjela mouth ulcer gel to the blister. It works better if applied overnight and left to dry. The blister will not have disappeared but will have dried out significantly and can be dressed.
- Sounds awful (perhaps any medics can tell us why it works) but for athlete's foot – let the dog lick your feet! There must be something in their saliva – yuk; but it works!
- Always carry a couple of cable ties in your rucksack; they are ideal for temporary repairs on boots (sole comes away) and on rucksack straps.
- Always pack Drapolene when going on a walking holiday! Designed to soothe babies' nappy rash, it also provides immediate and long-lasting relief to chafing of private bits(!) caused by sweaty underwear!
- Keep a foot cooling spray (with peppermint) and a spare pair of dry socks in the car. As soon you get to the car after a long walk take off sweaty walking socks, spray your feet with cooling spray and let your feet 'breathe' until they are dry.
- Use supermarket freezer bags with strip seals as a map case, mobile phone protector, storing keys, money, first aid kit, mess tins, and any other hiking bric-a-brac They keep things bone dry, even in your pockets.

If you are walking abroad, some of the rules and etiquette may well be different but, assuming you go with a specialist tour operator, you will be fully briefed. However if you do go venturing off abroad on your own, again it is worth listening to the advice of John Robinson, who often goes walking in Spain.

"Rural Spain has a rich legacy of tracks – indeed most rural roads can be considered to be such. Particularly notable are the mule-tracks, which go everywhere and can do some surprising things. However it does not seem that there is the same legal situation in Spain as in the UK regarding the preservation of tracks, and many have disappeared. This is often a result of the building boom – tracks get concreted over to provide better access to new developments.

Development itself destroys tracks, while the extension of the motorway system writes off others. There are doubtless many attractive walks, whether along the coast, up in the hills or even just wandering round places. The trouble is finding them. The Spaniards may or may not be great walkers (you should see the pace at which some of the goatherds move), but they know where they're going locally, and don't need signs.

The only pressures come from people on holiday and the northern European ex-pats who live there and who like a walk. Maps are various and not very good. They are rarely up to date and are not comprehensive. Their design is not up to OS standards and they lack detail. This is not entirely the mapmaker's fault. Get up in the hills and there is no detail. This is not England with its fields, woodlands, etc. These hills are featureless and identical. There's the occasional cottage, which may be marked, or it may not, and unless you know where you are, you don't know the difference. This isn't to say that there's no interest – there's lots of nature, views and so on, not as diverse as England but different, exotic even.

I rely on locally produced guides of the *Ten walks round Maro* variety. While still to be treated with some caution, these are the main method of finding your way about. In some localities, there are special routes, the *Rutas Turisticas*, which are marked with an increasing number of directional signs, but trying to get information from the tourist offices is just that – trying.

Spanish paths tend to be rugged and, in the hills, steep, so good footwear is important and a stick may be very useful. Since the sun might shine at any time of the year, a sun hat and plenty of water are essential. In the higher hills, a compass might be useful, but only if you know where you are to begin with."

If you lack confidence in navigation and reading maps, five-day courses are available at The **National Mountain Centre** (*www.pyb.co.uk*) at Plas y Brenin in Snowdonia. Expert walkers teach you all the basic skills, techniques and, most of all, the confidence you need to travel further in the hills under your own steam.

If all this sounds a bit daunting, I referred earlier to a travel firm called **Inntravel** whose website carries some interesting travel logs. One describes a walking holiday along the Catalan coast on the Costa Brava, and seems to provide the sort of mix of punishment and pleasure that might be a good first–heart op/attack venture, although it is not cheap.

This is certainly the nearest you will get to a sybaritic walking holiday and seems a long way from the blisters and sweaty crotches cautioned against above. Sweaty crotches in a luxury hotel? I think not, so the walks need to be of a relatively gentle (and genteel for that matter) nature, if you are opting for the luxury end of the walking holiday market. Here is one description of one such sybaritic exercise, if that is not a contradiction in terms.

"Set in lush gardens, the 4-star Hotel S'Agaró in the exclusive little bay of the same name is the sort of place where, if it hasn't quite sunk in yet, it soon dawns on you that you are on holiday and can forget about work. We arrived there in the mid-afternoon, having flown into Barcelona earlier in the day, and taken the train north to a small town called Caldes where we were met by a friendly taxi driver who drove us to the coast. The hotel's large terrace and bar beckoned, but even more tempting after a day of travelling, was the outdoor pool, and we enjoyed a leisurely swim before dinner.

After a good night's sleep, we headed down for breakfast the following morning. It was gone 9 o'clock (it had taken us less than 24 hours to fall into the Spanish pattern of life with their later meal times!) and the sun was already high in the sky. We ate on the terrace of the breakfast room overlooking the sea, a lovely start to the day, and it was then that I realised that we were in for a thoroughly relaxing week.

It was with a tingle of excitement that we set off from the hotel a little later. This first walk turned out to be fairly typical of the week – we followed the Cami de Ronda, a broad path that hugs the coastline just a few metres above the glittering sea. We walked from tiny cove to tiny cove, crossing the occasional small headland. Pines lined our path, lending a little welcome shade without interrupting the views. It was very easy to navigate – we hardly needed to refer to the walking notes – by keeping the sea to your right all the time, it was impossible to go wrong! Just as we were beginning to feel peckish, we rounded a bend in the path and saw a restaurant on the promenade ahead.

We both opted for a Catalan salad and, this being a holiday after all, decided to indulge in a bottle of wine to wash it down. Well aware that there was no rush – we'd looked at the map and seen that we didn't have much further to go – we took our time, enjoying the views across the sandy beach to the sea. The last part of the walk took us around a sweeping bay and through Palamos, a bustling town with a pleasant, authentic atmosphere, where groups of elderly men played boules in the central squares.

The hamlet of La Fosca and its quiet little beach is just on the other side of Palamos. The Hotel Ancora is a friendly hotel with an outdoor pool set just a couple of minutes away from the seafront. Its restaurant has a particularly convivial feel and is popular with locals. The speciality, something you should definitely try during your stay, is gambas de Palamos – huge, juicy prawns served dripping with garlic butter. Our next day's walk was different to the first in that it took us inland as well as along the coast, making for a varied, enjoyable day. In the scented pine woods behind the coast, we felt very much away from it all – it was just us and the sea, which we could still see below us."

Ian Lloyd is a web designer who likes writing about his travels (*www.lloydi.com*) – although he complains that no one pays him for his trouble. He recently walked through the 16 km Gorge of Samaria said to be the longest in Europe, situated in the White Mountains in West Crete.

His description captures well why, apart from the benefit of exercise, most walkers forgo the luxury described above – even if they could afford it in the first place – for the satisfaction of achieving a specific goal.

"0400 and the alarm clock woke us up. What were we thinking? Samaria Gorge was a fair old distance from our apartments in Chersonisos, which meant a very early pick-up (0505 am).

For much of the coach journey to Samaria I was asleep, my head bouncing off the bus window with only a flimsy curtain as a buffer. The views were quite spectacular the nearer we got to our destination. Our guide for the day, Alan, was chatting away at the front of the bus on the microphone but either the microphone was broken, the loudspeakers were out of order or Alan was taking part in a whispering competition

Whatever he was saying, I hoped it wasn't important. It later transpired that while I was asleep, he explained about some poisonous flowers that we should avoid, so perhaps a louder or better microphone/speaker/guide would have been wise.

Alan had provided everyone with a schedule for the day's walking. The idea was not to race, not to compete with each other, but to take it at your own pace. The chart suggested arrival and departure times for fixed rest points or lookouts and also suggested how long to stop at each point. To make sure that nobody got left behind, Alan waited for 30 minutes at the start of the walk (a place called Omalos) before setting out himself – something he would normally do three times a week. The plan was that if anyone in our group spotted him walking past – and he was easy to spot given his red T-shirt and trousers – they should stop him.

We trudged down 'the wooden staircase', the first part of the walk that took everyone deep down into the gorge, and the only section that had handrails. That was the easy part. The most difficult thing about this first section was stopping yourself going too fast – something to do with gravity. Once it levelled out a little, we bade farewell to the handrails and started to get used to the uneven rocky pathways that we would be walking along and clambering over for the next six hours.

While this was under a half marathon in length (approximately 11 miles), I wouldn't imagine people trying to do this too quickly, but there are exceptions – Alan had told us about a man who, just a fortnight previously, managed to make it through the gorge in just over two hours.

The temperature was not too bad, thankfully – in the early 30s. In the first couple of hours, it was fairly easy going. Sure, there were some sections that were challenging, and you had to be very careful where you put your feet so that you didn't slip or twist an ankle. I remember passing the 5km mark and thinking "Wow, that didn't take long". Although it was not a race, we did find ourselves checking our arrival times at each lookout point against Alan's suggested timings, and at each point we seemed to be gaining – 15 minutes ahead, then 25, then 40.

One of the best things about walking through a place like this is that you don't need to be too concerned about getting thirsty. There's no need to carry lots of water (which can soon weigh you down), as the fresh water in the streams is good enough to drink.

Close to the halfway point, we rounded a corner and saw a truly strange sight ahead of us. Either side of the established pathway was a 'field' of cairns – small stones which people had taken to piling up into small ... erm, piles. One of the other walkers said that you see them on walks in England, and that they signify an 'offering to the four winds'. A little thank you for a safe journey so far. Evidently a lot of people had been very thankful so far.

We kept bumping into a lady who explained several times what these stones meant. Our fellow walkers were generally quite distinctive and we gave them nicknames: Noah, a large-set man who looked like the professional walker with his big boots, chunky socks, massive staff (which, along with his grey hair, earned him the Noah tag) and steady pace; Lara (as in Croft), so named because of her attire: tiny shorts, crop top and her even quicker pace (overtaking her and her boyfriend gave us the greatest satisfaction); The German bodybuilder and his other half. They were wearing his-and-hers military sports gear in khaki cotton.

The halfway point was the long abandoned Samaria Village, just a stone's throw away from the equally ruined Church of Santa Maria (from which Samaria got its name). This was our cue to take a decent rest, eat our sandwiches, top-up the water bottles again and watch the *kri-kri* goats bound up rocky walls that looked impossibly steep. However, the rest timings were there for a reason: after this much walking (8km so far) over such terrain, a long rest is not advisable lest the calf muscles decide to seize up. So we obeyed the recommended 20 minute stop and then soldiered further on into the gorge.

From here on in, it just got harder. The sun rose to its highest point and there were fewer shady places. The water top-ups became more frequent and the walking became more like a mindless trudge – the legs picked up the feet and put them down, but the control we had early on was going. This was the point that most people, I imagined, had accidents – weary muscles, aching feet and slippery rocks are not a good combination, even less so if the path you are on is overlooking a deep drop to a dried up river bed below. We both took extra care at this point; we also noticed that all those gains we'd made in time earlier had well and truly slipped away. No more ten-minute gains to be had now.

The gorge walls started to get closer to each other and we knew that we were getting nearer to the Iron Gates – the most photographed section of the gorge (on just about every promotional leaflet) where only three metres separates them. Or at least it seemed we were getting nearer, but it was perhaps a good hour after these first tentative signs that we reached the gates themselves.

From here on in, things seemed to get easier again. It was a little flatter and there was also the promise that we were nearing the end of the trek. However, even when we reached exit control (where they collect your tickets and work out how many have not been handed in and hence how many people the rescue parties need to look for), we were not home and dry yet – there was still a good half an hour of walking under the blazing sun.

Finally we exited the gorge proper and got back on to blissfully flat paving – our route to the meeting place, a bar called *Gigolos* in a village called Agia Roumelli. Alan chose this spot, as it was easy to spot the ferry that we needed to catch out of this seaside village, while simultaneously being able to nurse a well-earned beer.

As we had got there reasonably early (about an hour ahead of our schedule), I had time to take a dip in the beach, a peculiar mixture of extremely hot black sand and the most crystal clear water I'd seen since drinking out of the stream earlier in the day. A perfect way to round off a very tiring day."

Part Two

A Traveller's Tales

Chapter 6

At the Cutting Edge

I was dozing on the sofa one Monday evening after a double helping of *Coronation Street*, when the phone woke me.

A disembodied voice said: "Hullo, this is Jane. I was just wondering whether you had any dietary requirements." She sounded English, so she obviously wasn't cold-calling from an overseas call centre. On the other hand, who else would be interested in what I ate, particularly at 2130 on a Monday night?

I must have sounded slightly perplexed, although I did manage to mutter that I was allergic to shellfish. "That's not a problem, we can't afford anything as fancy as that anyway" she replied with a hearty chuckle.

"I'm sorry, but who am I talking to?" I finally asked, feeling that this conversation was becoming surreal.

"Oh sorry, I forgot to say. Silly me. I'm your National Trust leader next weekend." Of course, I should have realised. I had booked to take part in a National Trust working weekend at Cliveden in Buckingamshire, and it was standard practice for the volunteer leader to ring round all the lambs to the slaughter in advance, to ensure they knew what they were letting themselves in for.

I had done several of these weekends in the past, but this was the first one since my heart attack. They usually consisted of a couple of days' hard graft, clearing undergrowth or building fences or stone walls, so I was slightly nervous that I might not withstand the course.

I didn't think Jane needed to know of my fears, however, as I suspected she might fuss around, which was the last thing I wanted.

After all, one of the points of testing your stamina is to exercise your own judgement as to how much you can cope with.

I had worked at Cliveden before, building a fence to keep dogs out of a field full of expensive racehorses. It is not one of the National Trust's more accessible properties, as the house operates as a luxury hotel and the grounds are only open to the public for a few months each year.

The original house was built in 1666 for George Villiers, the second Duke of Buckingham, but burned down in 1795. Its main claim to fame was that the first performance of 'Rule Britannia' took place in a theatre in the grounds in 1740. The house was eventually rebuilt but burned down a second time. However, it was third time lucky, because the current house, designed by Charles Barry, has survived more than 150 years in the Buckinghamshire countryside.

The Duke of Westminster – worried that there was a bit of England he didn't own – snapped the house up in the 1870s, but he then sold it to the Astor family. From 1919, it was the home of Waldorf Astor, whose wife Nancy was the first woman Member of Parliament.

During the 1930s, the house became a very fashionable place for prominent figures in both politics and the arts, to meet and plot and take part in famously lavish parties. This group of nobs and snobs became known as the Cliveden Set, and was very vociferous in calling for an appeasement with Hitler.

The house again became notorious during the early 1960s, when it became the centre of the Profumo scandal. For those readers not old enough to remember, the story involved the cabinet minister John Profumo, who first met a showgirl called Christine Keeler while both were visiting Cliveden. This meeting set off a train of events involving Russian spies, shared confidences in a swimming pool, and a juicy trial that kept the newspapers happy for months.

Despite the fact that the Astors still lived in the house at this time, they had already handed it over to the National Trust. When they moved out in the late 1960s, Cliveden first became an overseas study campus for Stanford University, and then a luxury hotel, which has had a fairly chequered history. In the meantime, the gardens have been maintained by the National Trust in splendid style, and I was off to make my small contribution to their maintenance.

The National Trust runs 'base camps' all over the country, which are either converted houses or barns with basic sleeping, washing and cooking facilities for the volunteer troops. Sometimes they are close to the work site, at other times some way distant. Our group was due to stay at the Chiltern base camp, which consisted of two barns on the Ashridge Estate near Tring. The facilities were fairly basic, but adequate if you are used to youth hostels or camping. The loos flushed (just about), the showers were hot (most of the time), and the dormitories had solid bunk beds and surprisingly comfortable mattresses.

I arrived after dark, but managed to follow the instructions without too much bother. It was clear from the number of cars outside, that I was one of the last to arrive, so my entrance was relatively unnoticed. A party of around 10 was sitting around a large kitchen table drinking tea and eating what looked like home-made cake. "Hi I'm Jane we spoke on the phone," chirped a short, stocky lady whose voice I recognised from our surreal telephone conversation the previous Monday. "Have a piece of courgette cake – it's home made." I don't think Mr Kipling – or many others, for that matter – goes in for courgette cake so I had no reason to dispute its provenance. "Would you like some tea or coffee or a glass of my home made elderflower and parsnip wine?"

"Tea will be fine," I replied, wondering how I was going to get through the evening without having to taste her witch's brew.

The first 30 minutes felt a bit like the first meeting of an Alcoholics Anonymous group (not that I'd know, I hasten to add). Everyone introduced himself or herself and said how many times they had been on NT working holidays. First-timers were eyed up and down with suspicion, and an unspoken pecking order quickly formed itself.

I felt slightly smug being an old-timer. However this was tempered by the fact that I was clearly the oldest member of the party and I could sense that the others were assessing me like judges at an agricultural show, to see if I was likely to last the course.

At that moment, the outside door swung open and a grey-haired lady strode in. She had that air of authority which used to be the trademark of the teaching profession.

"Sorry I'm late. I'm Vera. No excuse. Live nearby, ha, ha, know what its like, ha, ha." She was definitely older than me, which improved my position in the pecking order, but I could see everyone looking at her with wary respect.

Every National Trust working group has at least one person who wants to talk about his or her job in enormous detail, and can usually keep up a two-day monologue with little difficulty. Our 'dish of the day' on this occasion was *Karen the Caterer*. She worked for one of those catering companies that provide inedible food for schools and meals on wheels, but she hastened to point out that she ran the staff restaurant of a mobile phone company, and that the food she produced was of a very high quality.

After two days, there was little we didn't know about the problems of cutting carrots, sterilising cooking pots and lump-free custard. We knew that she was too tired to cook when she got home, that her husband had an appetite like a bird and that her staff were generally unreliable.

But on this occasion, we had another competitor for the title of *Top Job Bore*. Melanie was a young marketing executive for a multi-national company, and it would seem that the entire empire depended on her skills. On the second evening, she laid out her spreadsheets across the kitchen table, so we all had to bunch up in one corner while the furiously scribbled across acres of paper with a selection of marker pens.

I might have been tempted to tip a bottle of elderflower and parsnip wine over her *magnum opus*, but it had all been consumed the previous evening by an Irish civil servant called Dana. and Kate, who worked in that bit of the civil service that investigates air crashes.

They had both got into a long and somewhat alcoholic discussion about divorce. This was a subject they both clearly knew quite a lot about, and they then moved on to whether the air crash lady should go out with one of her bosses who had been making suggestive noises the previous week. Apparently he was 40, lived with his mum and had never been married, so I found myself offering a few words of caution.

Although the leader had bought the food and cooked the first evening meal, everyone was expected to help with washing up, cleaning and cooking other meals. Surprisingly enough, most people were pretty good at mucking in, although it was possible to skive off if you did it discreetly.

Unusually, the first night passed off peacefully. The golden rule of all communal sleeping is that there is always one person who could win a gold medal for snoring. Fortunately there were only three males in the party, and the other two slept silently. As usual, I had to pee in the night, but I couldn't be bothered to trek across the yard to the loos so I relieved myself under the stars – quite romantic in a strange sort of way.

Much to my surprise, Dana, the Irish civil servant, was surprisingly bright the next morning and appeared to have no signs of a hangover – perhaps the elderflower and parsnip hooch was non-alcoholic after all. There was a flurry of activity as breakfast was prepared, eaten and washed up, sandwiches and flasks were assembled, and boots and wet-weather gear piled into the minibus.

Vera appointed herself as navigator, and firmly planted herself in the front passenger seat, while everyone else obediently clambered into the back. After a few crashed gears, Jane got the hang of driving the minibus, and we set off through the chocolate box commuter villages of Buckinghamshire till we reached Cliveden an hour later.

On arrival, Clive, the National Trust duty warden, told us that we were to spend the next two days cutting down a large area of laurel from one corner of the estate. All I knew about laurel was that the Delphic priestess Daphne turned herself into a laurel tree to avoid being raped by Apollo, and that laurels leaves were placed on the heads of victors throughout the ages, especially at Olympic events and Roman games.

What I didn't know was that cyanide is found in the leaves of the laurel plant, and thus stops grazing animals from eating them – one of nature's clever little ways of giving plants and animals a chance of survival. Apparently ingesting moderate amounts of laurel leaves gives animals sufficient headaches and mild heart palpitations to steer them elsewhere. However, in ancient times, it was discovered that the distillation by evaporation of laurel leaves produced lethal concentrations of cyanide, and it later became the favoured poison of Adolf Hitler, Eva Braun and Hermann Goering, when they all discovered their time was up.

As you can imagine, therefore, laurel does not provide a very pleasant environment for wildlife in general, so with saws and loppers at the ready, we set off to slash and burn this poisonous enemy of the local wildlife.

The trick was to pair up with someone keener and stronger than you. National Trust volunteer groups are a microcosm of the world. There are always a couple of loners who like to work quietly and methodically on their own. If you are having a bonfire, you always find one potential pyromaniac who fanatically stokes it with a demonic look.

The chatterer invariably moves from group to group, doing very little work but engaging volunteers in conversation. This often turns out to be the group bore as well, although on this occasion, *Karen the Caterer* worked very hard, even though she talked without interruption about the efficacy of Weightwatchers, while wielding her loppers.

The strength and determination of some of the women in the group was awe inspiring, while the three males took a slightly more measured approach to the work in hand.

Dave had a thing about tree felling and eyed every tree as a potential target for his saw. We were under strict instructions only to cut down laurel trees, so he had to be physically restrained from cutting down others that looked perfectly healthy.

By 1100, penetrating drizzle had set in, but we didn't really notice, because the heat from the bonfire created a sauna-like effect. We were given 15 minutes off for stewed tea and digestive biscuits, and then half an hour at lunchtime to eat our sandwiches, which had somehow emerged from the breakfast scramble.

In a way that must be unique to the Brits, we sat in the rain, eating our lunch and making comments about how lucky we had been with the weather. Lucky? I suppose it wasn't snowing.

By 1600, we had made surprising inroads into the laurel and had created two bonfires that would have done credit to a team of Hell's stokers. It was quite surprising that a group of volunteers, who had actually paid for the privilege of slaving away in the Chiltern dampness, did far more work than would have been achieved by your average troop of British workmen. This may have been because we didn't get the opportunity to emulate them by loitering in the nearest greasy spoon until it was time to knock off.

Another characteristic of National Trust volunteers is that they always need a supermarket fix on the way back to base camp. As the wine stock had been demolished by Dana, Dave, John and Kate the night before – they got through four bottles of shiraz before resorting to the elderflower and parsnip brew in desperation – we all chipped into to pile up the trolley with new supplies of cheap beer and wine. Of course, I am obliged to sound a killjoy note at this stage, and point out that, tempting though it may be after a hard day's physical grafting in the open air, heart condition sufferers need to be wary of joining in the drinking sessions that usually round off the day on this kind of working holiday. Much as you need to be mindful of the fat content of local delicacies when travelling, a spot of restraint is called for as far as drink is concerned.

By the time we got back to the base camp we were tired and dirty. Inevitably, all four showers decided to throw a wobbly at this crucial moment, literally blowing hot and cold with wayward unpredictability. However, somehow we all managed to scrub up and Jane organised a work party to produce shepherd's pie and crumble for dinner.

I managed to escape the cooking rota, and decided that half an hour's kip on my bunk could be excused on medical grounds, although I felt surprisingly well, considering that my heart had taken quite a pounding over the previous eight hours. However, I did feel honour-bound to help with the washing up.

We planned to head off for the nearest pub after supper, but we all got talking and drinking at one corner of the table while Melanie the Tob Job Bore spread her papers out, and before we had even started getting ready to go out, it was past closing time.

Sunday morning saw another buzz of activity but this time we had to pack and clean up before setting off for our second day of labour. At least the sun shone weakly on our endeavours and, despite the rain, the embers of the two fires still glowed on our arrival at Cliveden.

Five hours later our job was nearly done. As I smashed through the last bit of laurel, I hit upon a boundary fence. Somehow it looked familiar and I realised that it was the fence we had put up on my last working holiday a couple of years ago.

I felt like I had come full circle and set off for home in a gentle glow of virtue. The National Trust also runs week-long holidays for the truly dedicated but I'm not sure if I could have coped with seven days of *Karen the Caterer* and her messianic fervour for the virtues of Weightwatchers and mass catering. On the other hand I felt a whole lot better after two days. After a week, I might have felt a totally new man.

Chapter 7

A Remote Dot in the South Atlantic

Not many people want to write a guide book to St Helena, a very remote spot in the South Atlantic. Mention the name, and those with a little historical knowledge will tell you that Napoleon was exiled and died there. Otherwise a blank comes over most people's faces. Furthermore, few publishers are prepared to pay an author the exorbitant cost of getting there. So when Bradt Guides (publishers of over 100 guides to obscure corners of the globe) discovered I had been there before and that, not only was I prepared to return, but had sufficient contacts to get my fares paid, a contract was shoved in my hands in a matter of days.

Then I stopped and thought for a moment. St Helena has no air access and is dependent on one small ship. It is also about 1,300 miles from the nearest decent hospital. There is a small hospital on the island with limited facilities, but if I had further heart problems, life could be tricky. Never mind. You do have to take risks from time to time, and I wasn't prepared to let this opportunity go.

The first time I saw St Helena was in 2004, a few months before I had my heart attack. It was early in the morning when I got my first sight of the island, looming like a massive lump of granite in the middle of nowhere. I immediately got a tingling sensation in my spine. I had read a great deal about the island and had dreamt of visiting it for many years. After seven days crossing an empty sea, the outline of my fantasy island suddenly came into view. Looming through the mist, however, my fantasy island had transformed itself into a solid lump of rock, and a rather forbidding looking one at that.

After we got off in St Helena, the ship departed for a side trip to

Ascension Island, before returning to the island a week later. For the first time in my life, I really felt that my fate was in the lap of the Gods and that I was a very long way from home and totally marooned.

Sometimes described as 'one big volcanic pudding', St Helena is one of the remotest spots on earth, 16 degrees south and five degrees, 45 minutes west, 1,200 miles from the nearest mainland (Angola) and around 1,800 miles from Brazil. Napoleon was its most infamous resident, having been exiled on this remote South Atlantic island by the British after his defeat at the Battle of Waterloo.

With no airport and only one ship servicing the island, St Helena is officially a British Overseas Territory but is, in reality, a colony, complete with a huge lumbering bureaucracy of expats and Saints, fussing over the lives of a mere 3,600 inhabitants.

The island is one of 14 UK Overseas Territories, which make up an exclusive club. They range from the tiny island of Pitcairn with its 47 inhabitants, set in the middle of the Pacific Ocean, to Bermuda, which has a population of 62,059 and is one of the world's major financial centres.

My first journey to St Helena started at Nelson Dock in Cape Town where the Royal Mail Ship *St Helena* was tied up. The dock was pretty rundown and passengers stood around in a bare shed, which contained little more than a few plastic chairs.

There was torrential rain and a near hurricane – hardly perfect weather for setting sail into the Atlantic on a relatively small ship. However, the elements took pity on us because the weather suddenly improved as we were about to set sail.

I had been on board the ship once before when she was docked at Cardiff, so I was unfazed by the fact that she could have easily passed muster as an elderly cross-channel ferry. She is one of only two remaining genuine passenger/cargo ships in the world and carries 128 passengers, 65 crew and officers and all of St Helena's needs, apart from fuel. She also acts as the single link between the thousands of Saints working in the UK, Ascension Island and the Falklands, and their families back home.

The RMS tries to replicate the old *Union Castle* service that called regularly at St Helena until the 1970s and the officers and crew are mainly Saints or British. I had been warned that she rolled quite a bit, even in calm weather, so I was grateful for the fact that I rarely get seasick. Nonetheless she carried a ship's doctor with a small surgery and a limited supply of drugs – although I am not quite sure what would have happened if someone had needed major medical attention.

The whole ambience was a microcosm of England 30 years ago. The passengers fell into three groups: half were Saints, returning from working abroad or from visiting their families in the UK. The second group consisted of advisers. For example, there was an urologist from Cape Town who was going to spend a week dealing with the islanders' waterworks problems, and an educational psychologist.

The third group were tourists – the majority from South Africa with a handful of British and Australians thrown in for good measure. Shortly after boarding, we had a fire drill which was followed by tea complete with curled up cucumber sandwiches, Madeira cake and tea. As we set sail, the loudspeakers blurted out a recording of a country and western song called *My St Helena,* composed by an American singer who had never been to the island, followed by a military band playing *A Life on the Ocean Wave* and *Rule Britannia.* For a moment, I thought we were going to get *God Save the Queen* and everyone would be expected to stand up.

Dinner was heralded by a dreadful rendition of *Food, Glorious Food* on the tannoy. I found myself on a table with an Australian divorcee of an uncertain age (who I finally shook off somewhere in Namibia – but that's another story), and a French nurse who was very religious and kept producing various tracts from her handbag.

Two of my fellow passengers at dinner were very quiet Saints. For the first two days they said very little other than to tell me that they worked for the British 'landed gentry'. After a lot of probing, it transpired that they had worked as housekeeper and handyman for the Princess Royal and told me that while HRH was actually very nice, her daughter Zara was 'a stuck up madam'.

The boat was like a small village with all the Saints sitting around sharing gossip. They were mostly of Indian and Chinese origin, reflecting the fact that St Helena was a major port of call during the heyday of trade between Europe and the Far East.

While they all spoke English and seemed to have several relatives in the UK, they mainly spoke a patois among themselves. The only bit of real excitement was the fact that the new Governor of the island was on board. This sounds very grand but actually he was a civil servant from the Welsh Assembly.

To pass the time, I took up with a couple of South African journalists – one wrote a sex advice column for the South African version of *Cosmopolitan*, while the other claimed to have been voted the tenth sexiest man in South Africa – a dubious claim to fame if ever I heard one. However we teamed up with the aforementioned Australian divorcee and a very bright 11 year-old Scottish lad, who had lived most of his short life in Bosnia and St Helena, to vanquish all comers at the nightly ship's quiz.

The voyage developed into a gentle pattern of eating, drinking, gossiping, playing deck games, sunbathing and more eating, only broken by two stops in Namibia. The first was in Lüderitz, a small port that used to be at the centre of the diamond industry, which seemed to be fast asleep at 1000 on a Sunday morning.

We were taken to Kolmanskop, a ghost town that had existed solely to service one of the largest diamond mines in the world. The mine itself was eerie. The main buildings were reasonably well preserved with a large theatre, gym, skittle alley and dining room, all of which were built to keep the workers happy. Most of the houses, however, were derelict and were rapidly being buried in sand.

The second call was at Walvis Bay, the only major port in Namibia, which until 10 years ago was retained by South Africa as an isolated outpost. I went on a 4x4 desert tour led by a reformed alcoholic called Chris, who kept stopping in order to show us lizards, side winder snakes, beetles and chameleons – the latter, despite their name, being surprisingly visible.

Chris showed us photographs of himself as a long blond-haired surfy. He said he was now a reformed character and that he firmly believed in creation as opposed to evolution because it was impossible for all these desert animals and plants to have evolved without outside help.

After this little diversion, there was nothing but sea for the next four days, though I did spot one rusty fishing boat and two dolphins. One night I managed to lose a skittles match to the Governor-elect. It was strange to think that this pleasant and down-to-earth chap was about to get pretty much total control over the lives of 4,000 islanders.

However, he said that he had instructions from the Foreign Office to keep things as informal as possible. Therefore, unlike his predecessors, he would not be wearing the traditional plumed hat and other paraphernalia at his swearing-in ceremony.

On the day before we reached St Helena, there was a general air of anticipation. The Saints were nearly home after a long time away. The visitors, after a week on an empty ocean, were soon to be on dry land again

We had instructions to pack our bags and leave them outside our cabins for collection. We then had to fill in various immigration forms. I did object to paying a £12 entry tax, given that the whole island is entirely supported by a grant from the UK taxpayers, but thought it wiser to keep silent on the subject.

We were treated to a final night's barbecue on deck with a disco knocking out sixties and seventies favourites – somehow a suitable finale for this curiously old-fashioned voyage.

I was slightly confused when I was told I would be travelling by 'air taxi', along with a couple from St Helena who were recovering from surgery carried out in the UK. I had hurt my leg in Cape Town and was not considered safe to scramble onto the launches that came out to meet us. The 'air taxi' turned out to be a metal cage, which was winched off the ship onto a floating barge that took us to the harbour. The other passengers had to scramble down a ladder onto a small launch, as there were no dockside moorings on the island.

We landed at Jamestown, a pretty little Georgian port, snuggling in a small valley. I was met by Patsy and Arnold who were to be my hosts for the week I was to spend on the island. After waiting for what seemed like ages for the baggage to be unloaded, I was eventually driven to their bungalow located just above Jamestown along a tortuously bendy road that climbed round the cliffs.

The bungalow had a colonial feel with a big veranda overlooking the sea. I didn't hang around for long, as I was anxious to see the Governor's swearing-in ceremony. I couldn't believe how many policemen, firemen, boy scouts, girl guides, and so on, could be mustered to march past the new Grand Vizier, who had been allocated a limousine and a splendid mansion called Plantation House, which came complete with Jonathan, the island's 170 year-old tortoise.

There were endless speeches, some extraordinary hats and a feeling of unreality as I watched this archaic British village-like ceremonial in just about the most remote spot on earth.

Despite its severe rocky exterior, I soon discovered that the interior of St Helena is tropical, lush and varied in its scenery and wildlife. While the coastal strip that includes Jamestown is semi-desert, the interior with narrow winding roads consists of a series of ridges,valleys and tropical forests clinging to the mountainsides. One moment you are in the Lake District, the next in a tropical oasis. The only blots on the landscape are some of the houses, which seem to be built fairly haphazardly, and with little architectural merit.

Several thousand Saints work in the UK, the Falklands and Ascension, so they send money home and build houses for their retirement. Hence there seem to be more houses than people.

Once upon a time, St Helena made quite a decent income from growing flax, which was turned into the string that the Royal Mail used to bundle up our letters. Then some bright bureaucrat thought that rubber bands would be cheaper – and the St Helena economy promptly sank to the bottom of the South Atlantic. Now the island largely depends on UK Government subsidies and is run by a disproportionately large administration for what is, in effect, a large village.

Although there had been a murder shortly before my arrival, there is very little crime (after all where would you escape to?) and I quickly got into the habit of leaving my battered old hire car unlocked. I even ended up leaving the keys in the ignition. This car sometimes doubled up as a taxi and had a For Hire sign in the window, so I got flagged down from time to time.

Napoleon's house at Longwood is now a well-preserved museum owned and run by the French Government. Obviously the house, his tomb and the Briars, where he stayed for a while before Longwood was ready for him, are invariably visited by the modest number of tourists, particularly students of French history and are looked after by a resident French consul.

I did the tourist bit on a 1929 open top Chevrolet charabanc, which ground its way up and down steep and bendy roads with amazing ease. I resisted the chance to play golf (not that I knew how anyway) on the nine-hole St Helena Golf Course – possibly the most remote in the world. I visited the handful of hotels and sampled the few restaurants. I don't think you could sell this as a gourmet paradise. Virtually every meal I ate was plain English cooking circa 1960 with lots of frozen peas, boiled potatoes and stew. The hotels were quite old-fashioned, reminding me of the sort of hotels I stayed in as a child.

There was one smartish country hotel called the **Farm Lodge**, where five of us ate one night and where the food and service were pretty good. The main hotel in Jamestown, **The Consulate**, had spacious en-suite bedrooms and a good dining room, but when I was there, the owners were rigid about dining times (1800 sharp and no choice of food), which was understandably irritating to residents.

It must be said that St Helena's hotels and restaurants had something to learn about modern expectations. My fellow tourists felt that they were being dictated to and we were unable to have drinks and meals when it suited us. Nonetheless, the vast majority of visitors seemed very happy because the island is beautiful, everyone is friendly, and they had the satisfaction of knowing they were far from the madding crowd and unlikely to meet anyone from back home.

Perhaps more importantly, the island is safe from snakes, poisonous spiders or malaria and the weather, generally, was warm and tropical.

Heart recoverees need to take plenty of exercise, and indeed, there is no such thing as a level road or path on the island. There is excellent hill walking available with a good variety of plant and bird life for those with an interest in nature. There is also a decent open-air swimming pool and some good sports facilities at the main school.

For those with a naturalist bent, there are around 100 indigenous plant species that have survived, but the eager 'twitchers' among us were disappointed that most of the millions of breeding South Atlantic seabirds had disappeared. Some common sea birds such as the fairy tern are still to be seen, and there are several introduced species, but there is only one bird – the wire bird – that is exclusive to St Helena.

The wire bird is believed to have originated from the plover family and was blown across from Africa. It certainly looks similar to a plover but is larger, with longer legs and more rounded wings.

However even this symbol of St Helena – it appears on logos everywhere – is disappearing fast. In the last ten years the wire bird population has declined by 20%, but no one was quite sure why.

Sadly I wasn't able to walk much, as my knee had become steadily more painful while I was in St Helena, so it became necessary to try out the hospital facilities. I would be less than honest if I said that they were anything other than basic.

The two Indian doctors and the handful of nursing staff could have probably dealt with a heart attack, although I doubt that they had the latest clot-busting drugs. Forget about complicated heart surgery – cardiac cases would have to wait till the *St Helena* called again on its way back to Cape Town.

Drugs seemed to be at a premium and the physiotherapy I was offered was well intentioned, though not particularly effective. Strangely enough, the unavailability of sophisticated medical facilities doesn't seem to be a huge problem. As far as I could make out, most Saints seem reasonably healthy and live as long as the rest of us in our considerably more polluted environment.

But, dear readers, I have digressed from the tangled affair of Sandra, the Australian divorcee, whom I mentioned earlier. A former publican in Sydney, she had abandoned three former husbands in Oz, in order to catch up with a British man she had met on top of a Peruvian mountain and was now working on the island.

It was pretty obvious to all but Sandra, that the chemistry had somehow disappeared somewhere between Peru and St Helena. Sad to say, like poor Paddington Bear, Sandra was 'not wanted on the voyage' any more, and by the time she woke up to this unpalatable fact, there were few people who were unaware of her dilemma.

We all felt for Sandra's dented *amour propre*, and did our best to console her. She moved into the South African sex adviser's self-catering flat, and we managed to get her a passage on the next ship back to Namibia. Thus my proposed solo onward journey through Nambia, became not so solo as we left St Helena behind.

I left St Helena that first time with mixed feelings. I knew that I had been somewhere very different that very few other people would bother to visit. There was something surreal about seeing Royal Mail vans and British police uniforms on this remote rock.

When I returned two years later, post heart attack, a final

decision had been taken to build an airport but due to the complicated and controversial nature of the project, it is unlikely to be completed until 2012 at the earliest. So when I got off the boat the second time, I felt quite reassured to see a massive Norwegian tanker, moored off shore. If anything happened to me, I was sure those nice Scandinavian sailors would whip me on board and set sail for the nearest decent hospital in South Africa.

Fortunately I remained fit and healthy throughout this second visit, although I worked fifteen hour days, collecting information, interviewing people, exploring the island, trying out the few restaurants and then writing up my notes.

There are very few places in the world where you cannot get airlifted out of danger and into hospital. St Helena is one of those. Once the airport is built, there is little doubt that it will become an unusual but comfortable holiday destination. But its current unique isolation gives it a special *frisson* – particularly if you have a health problem. One day, no doubt, St Helena will become a favourite of the travel supplements, but they will certainly kill it for those with a taste for the unusual and isolated. In the meantime, get there while you can by ship.

Chapter 8

Viva Espana

74 year-old Bob from New Mexico spends eight weeks every year as a professional Santa Claus at his local shopping mall. When not required for his seasonal duties, he and his wife Joanne, set off for Spain which they have adopted as their second home.

Don't underestimate how seriously professional Santas in the States take their calling. There is even an Amalgamated Order of Real Bearded Santas although fortunately, the 250 female members are not required to have a permanent beard.

Bob and Joanne have also discovered a third home from home – **Pueblo Inglés** (Englishtown) – a language school that hires 'anglos', on an expenses-only basis, to talk non-stop English for 13 or 14 hours a day with a group of Spaniards.

The Spaniards are an eclectic bunch – ranging from business people, actors and artists to dentists, journalists, car dealers and nuns. They pay £1,200 to immerse themselves in our language for a week, in the hope that they can short cut classroom language learning.

Pueblo Inglés has three base camps. I had signed up to work in one that was based in a brand new hotel just outside La Alberca, in the province of Castilla y Leon, about an hour and a half south of Salamanca. La Alberca is a drop-dead gorgeous little town and was the first of Spain's country villages to be declared a national historical monument.

It is bursting with quaint, overhanging, half-timbered houses, many of them surrounding the Plaza Mayor, an irregular square bordered by columned arcades. Some of the restoration would not pass muster in the UK; B&Q doors and windows seemed to have found their way incongruously into the stunning old houses.

La Alberca was a stopping place for pilgrims on their way to Santiago de Compostela, and cave paintings in the surrounding hillsides testify to even earlier visitors. In the Middle Ages, Spain's Moorish, Catholic, and Jewish cultures came together in the town, each leaving a subtle influence on the local architecture, music and food. Food is still a big selling point The acorn-fed *serrano* ham of this region – made from small, black Iberico pigs known as *pata negra* – is considered the best in the world. It's certainly the most expensive. When commercially exported to the United States, a whole ham on the bone can cost more than $500.

Bob, Joanne and myself were sitting around the fire in the splendid sitting room. Bob looked me straight in the eye, with Joanne sitting supportively by his side. 'Just imagine being a child again and you are sitting on Santa's knee in his grotto in the shopping mall. Tell him all the things you want for Christmas and Santa will do his best to grant them to you.'

Lest you think there was something odd about Bob, apart from his apparent addiction to dressing up as Santa Claus, I must hasten to add that we were preparing one of the many Anglo-Spanish plays and sketches that play an important part in the **Pueblo Inglés** experience. I had never done anything like this before, but Bob and Joanne had taken part in eight of these programmes and knew what was expected of us.

The people who run **Pueblo Inglés** maintain that conventional language training is like learning to swim in the shallow end of the pool. The instructor holds you underneath so that you are level with the pool surface and you then perform the new strokes being taught. If you flounder, you don't get any water up your nose. We were told that we should want our pupils to cough up half the pool. Why? Because that's what often happens to them in a real-life language situation. In an English class, if a student makes a mistake, the teacher corrects him and that is that. It is like a flight simulator. If you crash, you don't die.

They argue that they want to expose Spaniards to real English: to the real McCoy, not to a watered down, standardised version of the language. They maintain that most English teachers do the latter and, ultimately, they do their students a disservice. We were told to expose our new Spanish 'friends' to everyday language as they might hear it on the streets. Don't worry if they 'gag a little', we were warned, 'because the students will have no choice but to meet the flow head on and digest it'.

Few of us spoke much Spanish and even fewer were trained teachers, yet we were expected to shove English down these benign Spaniards' throats until they gagged.

So how on earth did I find myself in this situation? I had only been out of hospital a couple of months, when I decided to try to learn some Spanish. As I Googled my way through the labyrinth of Spanish language schools in Madrid – I had been told this was the only place to learn classical pronunciation – I clicked onto **Pueblo Inglés**'s website for no particular reason, only to discover it taught English to Spaniards.

However an article from the *Irish Times*, which had been pasted on the site's home page, caught my eye.

How does a seven-day stay in a picturesque village in the mountains of Spain sound? And how does it sound if you add in free room and board, and interesting company? These aren't trick questions – this is the deal offered by a language school with offices in Madrid, Barcelona and Granada, which specialises in helping professionals whose first language is Spanish to improve their conversational English by isolating them in said village for seven days with a group of English speakers. The Spanish speakers pay, the English speakers stay free – they just have to live up to their name and speak English to the Spanish speakers, morning, noon, and night, through meals, excursions and dedicated 'talking time'. That's the exchange – your holiday for your conversation. Everything except your transport to and from the Madrid pick-up point is paid for. If you are naturally outgoing and in need of something different ... put yourself in line for one of the upcoming sessions.

It was late at night, I couldn't sleep and **Pueblo Inglés** provided an online application form. What the hell? I had nothing to lose, and even if it was some sort of sales gimmick, I could bring matters to a close when my credit card details were demanded.

Surpisingly, it turned out to be a completely genuine proposal. Within 24 hours I had been accepted, a date and location allocated and a list of what-to-do-next instructions was dished out. The main instruction was to book an airline ticket to Madrid and provide evidence of having done so. The reason for this came down to one word: commitment. If the school saw that you had booked your ticket, it was pretty sure you would turn up on the appointed day.

On the one hand, it surprised me that several Americans were prepared to shell out several hundred dollars of their hard-earned cash, and give up 10 days of very scarce holiday to take part, particularly as the outfit made no secret of the fact that it was a highly profitable business. On the other hand, many of the American participants came from the more remote parts of the USA such as New Mexico, Montana and West Virginia, and therefore this was a unique opportunity to plug into a world that would be largely outside their experience back home. Thanks to Easyjet, I only had to fork out £50 plus a hotel room for a night in Madrid.

Over a period of six weeks before I was due to fly to Spain, I received a series of e-mail newsletters which were carefully graded to whip me into a frenzy of anticipation and excitement. The first newsletter gave us an idea of what was in store.

You will not be left alone during your week in Pueblo Inglés! Alvaro has trained a group of young and dynamic people, who like him, have incredible people skills and will be able to make sure the programme runs smoothly, that the hotel service is at its best and that you have the best week ever. They will be your BIG BOSS and will be with you 24 hours of the day. Even if you can't physically see them, they are there, watching everything that goes on!

In addition to your Big Boss, and your on-site leaders, you will be accompanied during the whole week by one of our best kept Pueblo Inglés secrets: your Master of Ceremonies who will be chosen from Greg Standford, Brian Bolles, Mike Schaupp, Davy Johnston & Rob Grams. One of these vivacious characters will act as monitor and be the right hand to the programme director. Their love for theatre, big groups of people and pure fun are the keys to make sure you are well entertained. They are always on the prowl. During the programmes, they'll grab some of you at different times and convert you into actors, performers and entertainers – with two to four hours of rehearsal. So, if you don't want to be picked out of the crowd let them know or hide well!

The second newsletter seemed almost too good to be true. Ever since I was a small boy, I have been in trouble for talking too much, so I had to pinch myself when I read the following:

Talking and listening – Are you a good talker? Are you a good listener? If we had to choose between only good talkers or only good listeners for this Pueblo Inglés experience, we would opt for the talkers. Why? Because understanding a foreign language well is much more important than speaking it well. You can learn to speak another language perfectly, but if you can't understand your counterparts, then what use is speech? You can acquire a good command of the structure of the language and be quite agile in reproducing it. However, this will mean very little if you are unable to follow the crosscurrents of discussion that so often characterise business and social get-togethers. Therefore, we would rather see you talking the ear off your Spanish friend than seeing him talk your ear off. There will be the same number of Spanish visitors as Anglo visitors. Anglos and Spaniards will lock horns for 110 hours straight.

It was like a child being offered free rein in the world's biggest sweet shop!

By the time I had read the third newsletter, I felt the psychological pressure mounting:

Dear friends, yet another newsletter comes to a close bringing us closer than ever to lift-off time. We now leave you with a quote from our beloved Don Quixote addressed to his trusted squire, Sancho Panza:

Amigo Sancho, you only get out of this life what you put into it.

And we say to you that the richness and delight of the upcoming experience in our little charming enclave, will depend to a very great degree on the zest and joy we put into making it rich and delightful. So, although it's still a bit early to start psyching up, it's certainly not too early to read up on Avila, Old Castile and Spain.

The fourth newsletter introduced us to our Spanish students:

During this week you will have the honour of spending a week with twenty Spaniards who are bursting with curiosity to learn all about your language.

Some of them are studying our Masters in English Programme, and as part of the programme, they will be making four trips to Pueblo Inglés. All of them have already experienced its magic and this will be their third programme. The two previous ones were so unforgettable that they can't wait to come back.

Others will be coming from the business world, where they often struggle to win their daily battles with the English language. They are terrified and don't know what to expect, so be gentle! Some of the companies they work for are.

And then we have a sprinkling of crazy people who simply love your language and want to jump in at the deep end with English! So, you will have the privilege of being their lifeguard.

Anyway, all of them have at least an intermediate level of English and are very curious to see what will happen in this special immersion talkathon in the beautiful Spanish countryside.

And then the final newsletter with the punch line:

Our string of newsletters has finally come to an end and we will be seeing each other in just a few days. You will be surprised at how instrumental you will be in effecting a genuine metamorphosis in the self-confidence of your Spanish friends. You will feel you have achieved more for more people in such a short period of time. And most importantly of all, you will have a wonderful time. You will not feel the direct impact of your responsibility in effecting the metamorphosis in question, because you will be sharing the responsibility with the rest of your fellow Anglos. You will ultimately be performing a collective miracle and you will see it happening as each day progresses. In the end, you will build that bridge for your new friends and you will feel happy and fulfilled.

After 24 hours in Madrid, staying in what was possibly the smallest hotel room ever devised by man, I finally got to meet my fellow Anglos with whom I was destined to perform a 'collective miracle'.

The staff had made great play of the *tapas* evening, at which we were going to meet our fellow Anglos before we set of for La Alberca. In practice we gathered in a bland classroom and were offered sandwiches with the crusts removed – more afternoon tea than Spanish *tapas*.

When we all had to introduce ourselves, I was slightly taken aback by the eclectic mix of Anglos. There were the aforementioned Santa duo from New Mexico, with their lifelong friend George; Carole, an elderly three-times divorcee; Pam and Bonnie, two folk singers from West Virginia; Liza Devine, a spiritualist and 'massage therapist' who announced that she was a 'citizen of the world'; Amanda and Maurice, a couple of backpackers who had only heard about **Pueblo Inglés** the previous day, but urgently needed free board and lodging; and Dorothy from Edinburgh via Newcastle, who had given up teaching to promote the virtues of cycling.

Then I encountered Miles from New Zealand, who had spent the last year refurbishing trains on the Bakerloo Line. He had an accent so strong I could barely understand him, so I wondered how the Spaniards would cope. Anne was a sparky Jewish 21-year old from Montana, who worked as a forest fire-fighter; Claire was a youth worker from Dublin, while Collette and Chantel were young Aussie backpackers.

The next morning we all piled into a garish pink coach, alongside about two-thirds of our Spanish tutees. Each Anglo had to sit next to a Spaniard. I sat next to Angel, a sales manager for one of the world's largest software companies. I had definitely drawn the long straw, as he was a really nice guy and spoke quite reasonable English. He had a British boss and we immediately struck up a good relationship.

The trip took around four hours and passed through a part of Spain I had never explored before. When we arrived, it was clear that the hotel was only partially built. The accommodation was in the form of two-storey houses, each with a sitting room and a fairly basic bedroom on the ground floor, with a much grander suite above.

Understandably, the Spaniards were allocated the more upmarket rooms, while the Anglo 'workers' got the more modest rooms below. This was somewhat unfortunate, as it led to an initial feeling of them and us. However this soon dissipated as we got down to the job of trying to turn our Spanish friends into fluent English-speakers in just seven days.

The pace was relentless. The day started at 0900 with breakfast where there had to be an even number of Spaniards and Anglos at each table. Then we were allocated our Spaniards for the following four hours. These were divided into one-hour sessions, when we either had 'one-to-one' sessions, during which we went for a walk up in the hills or sat in the lounge or terrace, talking about anything that came into our heads, or we held mock telephone conversations or conference calls, to get them used to conversing in English without the benefit of eye or body contact.

The 'one-to-ones' were pretty straightforward – we talked about everything you could imagine. One of the Spaniards was a very well-known actress who was due to launch a new film in Hollywood and didn't want to make a fool of herself on American chat shows.

Paco was a successful society dentist who was also an artist and art dealer, while Juan was in charge of Madrid's road system. There were a number of young women journalists and PR people; a pair of HR gurus from one of the big international accountancy firms; Maria, a physiotherapist who had decided that it would be more interesting to source and sell parts for railway engines; and a lay nun who edited an apparently controversial Catholic magazine.

One of my favourites was Alfonso, a car dealer with the accent and demeanour of Manuel in *Fawlty Towers*. He flew to Germany every week to buy a second hand Merc or BMW, then drove it at top speed back to Spain where he sold it from the forecourt of his car-wash establishment, of which he was inordinately proud.

The star of the show was a computer salesman called Antonio, who turned out to be rather a good comic actor, but had a tendency to stir up trouble when he didn't like something.

We were driven on by Brian, the master of ceremonies, who seemed to have a limitless supply of energy and good humour, and whose job it was to organise the various activities, lead, cajole and occasionally scold certain Spaniards who sat around late at night, reverting to their native language which was strictly *verboten*.

The one-to-ones were rather like confessionals. As we walked along country tracks, I was told intimate details of people's lives, including marital and work problems. I even had an animated discussion with the nun on the virtues (or otherwise) of celibacy.

The telephone and conference calls were a greater challenge than the one-to-ones, because you were given a specific subject and had to keep up conversation for an hour, without the benefit of eye contact or hand gestures. If things were getting sticky, I would lob in a controversial question to get them going. I got the best reaction when I asked them whether they thought women made better bosses than men.

With a dynamic economy and an extremely low birth rate, women are making considerable progress in piercing the 'glass ceiling' in Spain and so older men, in particular, tend to feel threatened.

However, Juan, Madrid's deputy chief road engineer, a highly cultivated but conservative 62 year-old, rather surprisingly said that his current boss was a woman and that she was by far the best he had ever had.

The Anglos and Spaniards were expected to perform some sort of mini play or entertainment each evening before dinner (held at a very Spanish 2100). Some of these were really quite imaginative and funny, but I did flinch somewhat when I was told, as I have already explained, that I would be performing with Mr and Mrs Santa (alias Bob and Joanne).

Although Bob told me to pretend to be a small boy and to sit on his knee, I really couldn't do this with a straight face. I was instructed to give him a run down on my wish list of presents, but in order to overcome my embarrassment at having to enact this bizarre little episode, I decided to challenge him on his training credentials and demanded to see his liability insurance certificate. I am not sure what was fact and what was fiction at this point, but the audience burst into laughter.

We then got roped into a disco-dancing championship – and I was grateful that my children did not have to witness their father cavorting with a lithe young Aussie. To make matters worse, we made it into the final, only to be pipped at the post by the aforementioned Juan, who surprisingly tripped the light fantastic with considerable agility.

On the last night, in true American style, we had an awards ceremony in a rather splendid baronial hall in La Alberca. This was taken quite seriously by Brian and Marisa, the administrator, although everyone else found it a bit of a laugh. I won the award for handling the best conference calls – an achievement I will be proud of for the rest of my life.

But the best moment of the evening was when the participant with the 'most improved English' was announced. By popular acclaim, the prize went to Miles, the Kiwi with the impenetrable accent who, by the end of the week, was actually able to make himself understood by most of the bewildered Spaniards.

Chapter 9

A Meeting with Polar Bears

The *Akademik Ioffe* is one of the curious postscripts to the Cold War. Built in 1988 for the Russian Academy of Sciences in Kaliningrad to carry out oceanographic research – and to keep an eye on US submarine activity – the ship is named after a distinguished Russian physicist who, ironically, got into trouble with Stalin because he was too supportive of western physicists.

She now picks her way among the icebergs of the Canada's Northwest Passage with boatloads of ornithologists and wildlife enthusiasts. They are prepared to pay quite a lot of money, and tolerate the discomforts of what amounts to a floating youth hostel, (though I am told the ship has now been upgraded), in order to cosy up to polar bears and visit places that are, to put it mildly, somewhat inhospitable.

They are also bewitched by the story of the search for a route through the Northwest Passage which has taken on almost mythical significance. The search for a water route through the Arctic, north of the Canadian mainland, to the imagined riches of the Far East, had being going on for 300 years. Early explorers such as Frobisher and Davis, failed to find a way though, and in 1819, the British naval commander Edward Parry reported that eastward-moving heavy ice floes were blocking the route north of Baffin Island, even in August.

Sir John Franklin finally reported an uncertain ice-free period for ships in August and September, but he perished before he could sail through. Eventually between 1903 and 1906, the Norwegian adventurer Amundsen travelled west and south of Lancaster Sound through Peel Sound and along the western Arctic coast. In 1954, the Canadian government icebreaker *Labrador* crossed the passage from west to east in a single year and in 1969, the American oil tanker *Manhattan* crossed from east to west with the help of a Canadian icebreaker. But despite this, the trade potential of the Northwest Passage remains unexploited.

Through a set of fortuitous circumstances, I was offered the chance to join the The *Akademik Ioffe* in Nanisivik, an iron ore mine on the tip of Baffin Island, with the only deep berth in the region.

My journey to the Northwest Passage began with a tortuous trip from London to Ottawa via Detroit and Montreal – the cheapest route available. I was bumped off the connecting flight to Montreal because of overbooking, but I saved myself a hotel bill and got a free transatlantic ticket into the bargain.

After a quick look round Montreal, I took a two-hour bus ride to Ottawa where I joined a charter flight for Nanisivik in Nunavut, formerly known as the Northern Territories. After four hours in the air, we stopped to refuel at Iqaluit, Nunavut's capital. To make matters more confusing, Iqaluit used to be called Frobisher Bay and is located on the Southeast of Baffin Island.

It looked like a true frontier town – a collection of shacks and a few larger buildings. As we took off again and flew north, I could see the land beneath us getting more and more barren. As we came into land I started to panic, as there appeared to be no civilisation of any sort and certainly no visible landing strip.

However, we eventually landed on a dirt runway at Nanasivik. The terminal building was a tiny portakabin covered in dust. A couple of ancient buses took us to what passed for civilisation – a community centre, dining room, dormitories and a shop called *Northern Stores*, selling bits and bobs, including incredibly expensive vegetables which were presumably flown in on the weekly flight. We were left to look around – not a lot to see, but interesting by its very nature.

We then were driven by bus right through the mine until we reached the *Akademik Ioffe,* tied up by the dock. She looked somehow out of alignment, with what appeared to be tiers of containers bolted to the top deck. In fact they were additional cabins which had been welded on after she had finished her life as a research (spy?) ship.

We clambered on board and were met by several young muscular characters, straight out of Central Casting. These guys were to be our lecturers, barmen and skippers of the Zodiacs, the inflatable rafts that were to be used for our various landings en route. At this point they were acting as glorified air stewards, telling us where to go and sorting out luggage. I was shown to my cabin, only to discover that someone else was scheduled to share it with me, despite the fact that I had been promised single occupancy.

So I went off to protest to Nigel, the ship's 'hotel' manager. He told me that the ship was full and there was nothing he could do. I could hardly disembark at this point, as I didn't fancy being stranded in Nanisivik. My cabin mate then stumbled through the door. Jim was a man of 82 who was still an active motorcyclist. He had just returned from a rambling tour of Iceland, but complained that the walks were too fast for him.

Luckily, I had grabbed the best bunk before he turned up, so that when he arrived, he made a huge fuss about not having a bedside table. However he managed to cobble one together by pulling out a drawer and lashing it to the bed.

We then went down to the dining room for the statutory welcome cocktail and had our first lecture on the dos and don'ts of life aboard. As is usual at the start of any group tour, everyone behaved like dogs sniffing around each other. It was clear that we had a very eclectic mixture of people on board. They included several leathery American ladies who normally, I would think, wintered in Florida, as well as many Canadians. There was also a Canadian TV film crew with a very self-important producer. He purported to be making a film for a Canadian TV cable channel and a corporate video for the tour organisers at the same time. I suspect that they were really freeloaders, as I was never sent a copy of the film, despite frequent promises.

Several of the passengers looked well heeled, but wanted to 'rough it' as a chic antidote to their winter sojourn in the Caribbean. They seemed to thrive on daily lectures about animal scat (poo to you and me) by learned naturalists. The expedition leader was a Scot called Laurie Dexter, who had lived in Nunavut for over 30 years and was also a well-known Arctic explorer, Anglican minister and jewellery craftsman.

I met a former MoD researcher from Tunbridge Wells, called Pam, who had been on 17 of these trips and an American called Karen, whom I had sat next to on the plane. She was a schoolteacher and seemed determined to play cards and get drunk. She had just come from a UK bird-watching tour and thought that, for some reason, the most wonderful place in the world was Filey. It certainly seemed odd to be listening to eulogies to this fairly undistinguished British seaside town in the middle of the Northern Arctic.

It didn't take long to realise that this was an extraordinary place. As soon as we cast off, we encountered our first icebergs which looked like floating white mountains. The reflection of the red sun on them was quite breath-taking.

The climate in the extremities of Northern Canada is so cold and dry that this region is classified as a polar desert. The temperature averages below freezing throughout the year, with a mean annual temperature of -14°C, and summer highs of only -1.5°C in the southernmost locations. Winter temperatures can reach below -30°C, which is well beyond the survival threshold for many plant species. Not only are these temperatures bitterly cold, but the mean annual rainfall is very low, ranging from 10–20 cm.

On our first night, we had a mediocre dinner, slightly better than school food, but served in much the same way. It was clear that we were not going to die from gastronomic over-indulgence.

Afterwards, most people seemed to peel off to bed, but I went to the bar and was reminded how to play pontoon by Karen. Chris, the slightly camp barman, told us that most of the Russian crew on the ship were formerley high-powered scientists working in fairly menial positions on board, because they couldn't get work as scientists any more. That seemed a sad postscript to the Cold War.

There was still bright sunshine at midnight, which was very disorientating. Eventually I went to bed, only to find Jim, my cabin mate, snoring away. I thus had a fairly sleepless night, not helped by the 24-hour daylight and the fact that Jim got up to go to the loo every ten minutes. He also shouted and sung in his sleep, so the next morning, I asked the chief steward if he could get me some earplugs.

We then had a briefing on how to avoid being eaten by polar bears on our first shore trip to Beechy Island. This was where the aforementioned British naval commander, Sir John Franklin, perished in his search to find the Northwest Passage. Tim, who presented the lecture, made out that the British only lionised those who had failed because although Franklin died a hero, he and most of his men perished without achieving their objective.

He also pointed out that two other British heroes – Scott and Shackleton – both failed in their missions and only ones who succeeded were Amundsen, who was a Norwegian, and the American Parry.

This anti-British diatribe was mildly irritating but luckily in the middle of all this there was a call for us to get out on deck, as there was polar bear swimming alongside. Sure enough we saw a magnificent specimen swimming in the water alongside the ship.

Lunch proved no better than dinner or breakfast, but was sufficient to sustain us for our first shore trip. It was very sunny but also chilly, and I knew that my newly acquired thermals and wet weather gear would come into their own.

We looked at the graves where Franklin's men perished. Their gravestones were made of fibreglass, the originals having been removed to a museum. We walked for about half an hour along the beach to Northumberland House, which had been built by a search party who came to find Franklin and had left him shelter and rations should he ever turn up. All that was left now was a mound of disintegrated barrels and metal rings, which had been left as a national monument. As Franklin disappeared about 150 years ago, I guess he was unlikely to show up now and even if he did, the rations wouldn't be a lot of use.

I was still without earplugs or even some cotton wool and Jim snored even more loudly the next night, so I was forced to wake him up before I actually hit him. Having just got to sleep at 0500, we were woken by an announcement that there were some rare birds on the port side and that so we should all get out there.

I dutifully shuffled out with my binoculars but had some difficulty finding whatever it was I was supposed to be looking for. More interestingly, we were now sailing along the south coast of Devon Island, apparently the largest uninhabited island in the world.

After breakfast, we put on our wet weather again and landed at Dundass Harbour, which had been disputed territory between the

Danes, Americans and Canadians for many years. In order to consolidate its claims of sovereignty, the Royal Canadian Mounties had built a police post there in the 1920s. This must have been the loneliest posting any policeman has ever faced! The buildings were now derelict (they were abandoned in the 1960s), but a psychologist from San Francisco did quite an amusing routine pretending to be an estate agent showing prospective purchasers around.

We saw several musk oxen which looked rather like bison. There were some amazing icebergs and on our way back, we circled round one which, from the shore, looked like a reclining polar bear. However our Russian Zodiac driver said he thought it looked like a woman reclining on her back.

We then landed at Croker Bay. We saw a polar bear walking across the ridge beyond us but I felt safe beside Brad, our six foot five guide who was an ex-US Marine helicopter pilot and looked suitably hard and mean: just who you might need when confronted with a hungry bear. He was holding a rifle, which I found quite comforting in the circumstances, although I had been told that polar bears weren't that impressed by rifle shots because they sounded like glaciers breaking up.

My ever-cheerful cabin mate Jim was fed up because he couldn't photograph the bears close up. Just for one unkind moment, I wished that the polar bear might fancy a slice of the old codger for his lunch.

However the bear had spotted something that looked more interesting than me or Jim for his lunch, so my grandchildren were (at least for the moment) robbed of the opportunity to tell their own children that their grandfather had been eaten by a polar bear. This would at least have replaced the prevailing family myth that my great-uncle was gored to death by a bull.

I then spotted a flock of Canada geese and seal pups and found that I was beginning to become quite intrigued by bird watching and the whole wild life scenario. The scenery was spectacularly beautiful and I felt overwhelmed by the notion that I was literally at the tip of the earth.

That evening I went again in search of cotton wool to keep Jim from driving me mad during the night. I found the ship's hospital, which was surprisingly well-appointed. The elderly and traditionally dumpy Russian female doctor did not speak any English, but with a degree of improvisation and sign language, I managed to borrow some cotton wool.

I am not sure that I would have wanted to go under her knife. Having said that, she had probably been a distinguished surgeon under the Soviet regime. When I went to bed, I stuffed the cotton wool in my ears and, for the first time, slept through the night with the help of a couple of Valium, which I had carefully saved for such an occasion.

As the trip unfolded, I found myself intrigued by wildlife, animals and birds in a way I had never really been before. A whole new vista was opening up.

My fellow passengers came from every walk of life and despite some being well into pensionable age and obviously arthritic, manoeuvred themselves in and out of the Zodiacs, and climbed up and down hills, with amazing dexterity. They might have looked like they were on their last legs, but they seemed to have more vitality and enthusiasm than some of the much younger passengers.

There were also the inevitable corporate lawyers and their children and one couple had three teenage sons on board, the youngest of which was determined to get into trouble wherever he went. One day he was caught climbing up the mast and then the next day found resetting the echo sounder on the bridge.

The best thing was that nobody – apart from Jim – complained about anything. They were here to enjoy themselves and were determined to make the most of the opportunities.

The third morning turned out to be grey and misty, yet being so far from anywhere with no civilisation for miles and miles around, it felt pleasantly mysterious. During the night, the ship had negotiated some tricky ice packs and the day turned out to be very eventful.

We landed on Low Point and went for a two-hour walk, clambering over rocks to look at 2,000 year-old foxholes and some Inuit ruins. The foxholes looked like brick ovens and, once the foxes had got in, they couldn't get out again and subsequently perished.

That afternoon we had a medical emergency. An elderly passenger, who had obviously had a stroke prior to the voyage, and didn't look like she should have been on board in the first place, was taken seriously ill and a decision was taken to evacuate her – easier said than done in this part of the world.

Fortunately we were quite near the Inuit community of Pond Inlet, which we were due to reach in 24 hours. The amazing and aptly-named Captain Beluga set off at full steam, navigating his way round a lot of ice.

The sick lady and her husband were eventually taken off somewhat precariously in one of the Zodiacs and were landed at Pond Inlet. Despite its remoteness, there was a computerised medical station where patients could be hooked up by telephone to a hospital in Iqaluit so that their condition could be diagnosed and monitored. We all silently hoped she would make it.

With the excitement over, I spent an hour with my grumpy cabin mate who, despite his 82 years, had just bought himself an £8,000, 1000 cc BMW motorbike, at the same time as he had moved into sheltered housing. Although he loved motorbikes, he hated televisions and computers and wouldn't have either in his home. I then had a conversation with a retired Russian urologist who lived in Los Angeles and wanted me to give him a detailed itinerary for a 28-day tour around the South of England.

With the stroke victim on dry land, we set sail for Albert Bay. It was a beautifully sunny morning, so I went up on to the bridge to see our arrival. The bay was absolutely spectacular and surrounded by steep cliffs. I walked for an hour up the side of the cliff but with only rubber boots, I was concerned about slipping. After lunch, we were told that although we were due to land in Pond Inlet (where our sick passenger had been delivered the previous day), the ice had closed in and it was going to be difficult to manoeuvre our way close to the shore.

I thought that Captain Beluga could do with my help so I clambered up on the bridge. Indeed there did appear to be an impenetrable slab of ice right ahead and it seemed that our landing would have to be aborted.

However, as we approached the ice, it turned out to be a mirage and everyone including the captain seemed quite perplexed as it literally disappeared and there was clear water ahead, enabling us to drop anchor only a short distance from the landing stage.

Pond Inlet had a sense of total isolation. Laurie, our team leader, had first come to this community as an Anglican minister thirty years ago, and everyone seemed to know him. The community had a population of 1,200, the vast majority of which were Inuit. The numerous babies were carried around in traditional slings, while their mothers were dressed in sneakers, Nike T-shirts and everyone seemed to be drinking Coke – a real clash of cultures.

The town was pretty tatty, but there was a brand new cultural centre and library, funded by the Canadian Government. We were given a display of traditional singing and dancing by three local girls. They sang the local *Ay ya ya* songs which consisted of making animal noises from the back of their throats. The idea was that the throat singer who kept a straight face longest, won the contest. This might have sounded bizarre but it was quite entertaining. A laconic youth then sang Inuit pop songs, accompanying himself on a Yamaha electric organ, which also seemed a little incongruous.

I then wandered up to the ubiquitous local Northern Store which turned out to be a mixture of supermarket and café where people were eating tinned spaghetti and chips. A notice on the wall announced that two of the four nurses were going on holiday, so the health centre would be understaffed. Therefore residents were reminded to 'eat well, buy Paracetamol and use lots of condoms'.

Although the setting at Pond Inlet was very beautiful, it had a slightly sad feel about it, although the locals seemed reasonably prosperous. There was a lot of construction work and fishing, and the community benefited from a daily air service to Iqaluit. It was, in many ways, surprisingly up to date, given its remote location. There was satellite TV, an admittedly very expensive internet connection and the store had electronic scanners. Yet despite all this, it felt quite desolate.

With little to do, it was hardly surprising that there was a serious birth control problem and that the Government had just had to build a second school to accommodate the rapidly growing population. Pond Inlet's only Canadian Mountie told me that there was a certain amount of alcoholism and sexual abuse, but not much theft because there was nowhere for anybody to escape to. Nevertheless, he said that the two cells were in frequent use.

I also met the current Anglican priest who said that in the winter there were congregations of up to 300 on Sundays, which I suspect would be the envy of many churches in England. However, this all changed in the brief summer, when everyone liked to fish and hunt.

On the way back, we toured round more glaciers on the Zodiac, but as we were shipping water at an alarming rate, I was relieved to get back on board the *Akademik Ioffe*. That night we set sail for Greenland. This gave us two days at sea, with a much-needed chance to relax. It was really quite hard work climbing in and out of Zodiacs, endlessly dressing and undressing to cope with varying temperatures and conditions. Nonetheless, I felt a lot better for all this exercise.

Thanks to Mike, the freeloading TV cameraman, who had suddenly produced three sets of earplugs, I had a peaceful night without the need for cotton wool or valium.

While we were at sea, Captain Beluga obviously wanted a rest from his talkative human cargo, so he announced that the bridge was out of bounds because of foggy conditions. There was no obvious sign of fog, but I guessed that he had been bought up in the Soviet era, where a pronouncement from an official had to be obeyed, so he probably never thought that his Western passengers might challenge his diktat.

Fortunately everyone took the hint and shuffled along to the main dining room to listen to Patty, a very talkative zoologist with a fascination for animal poo. Somewhat embarrassingly, I fell asleep during her talk on *Mammals of the High Arctic* but woke up for her husband's discourse on glaciers. You wouldn't have thought it would be possible to be anti-British about ice floes, but somehow he succeeded, much to my amusement.

As we sailed towards Greenland, the sea became quite rough and many passengers became seasick. Thank God I am a very good sailor, and despite the fact that my cabin was on the very top deck, and I could thus feel the heavy swell, my stomach behaved itself. In the early afternoon, we got our first sight of Greenland and were told that we should be able to land the following day as planned.

The whole surreal nature of this trip was underlined by a discussion several passengers and lecturers had on whether it would be possible to tow glaciers round the world to provide water for California or the Arab States. It didn't sound very practical, but was an interesting idea. Then we were invited to tour the engine rooms and to look at some of the scientific equipment that had been largely abandoned when the ship transformed itself into a cruise vessel. With my natural tendency to latch onto conspiracy theories, there was no doubt in my mind that this had been a Russian spy ship, and that the periscope and redundant computer and laboratory equipment had previously been in the service of the KGB.

As the night progressed, the sea got increasingly rough, waves crashed over the bow and in the murky light, I could see icebergs everywhere. I saw also a seal, which dived underneath the bow of the ship as a chunk of an iceberg split off with suitably dramatic effect.

It hardly seemed worth going to bed so I went up on to the bridge. As we inched our way round the ice, Umanaq – where we were heading – appeared to be packed with ice and as there was a high wind, we were told we might not be able to land.

Fortunately, Captain Beluga, as usual, proved to be pessimistic and managed to land quite easily. Umanaq turned out to be a pretty little town with a quaint harbour surrounded by wooden clapboard houses in greens and reds. There was a small museum and a post office. I called England for the first time since leaving Ottawa, with the aid of a vast satellite dish which towered over the town.

I took a walk around the back streets and realised that we were back in Europe, although geographically still on the North American continent. Greenland is a semi-independent part of Denmark, but left the European community 25 years ago.

I never expected to get mosquito bites in Greenland, of all places, but I developed three throbbing lumps on my face that afternoon after we landed in a small bay called Kilakitsoq. This was the site where the Greenland Mummies were found some years ago. They found six perfectly preserved mummies – two children, one with Down's Syndrome, and four quite sickly women. No one was sure whey they were there, but it looked as if they were killed and buried when the community could no longer cope with them.

That evening we had a barbecue on deck in bright sunshine. Some people sat inside the Zodiacs with the food balanced on their knees, while others leaned against the rails. Icebergs surrounded us, so once the sun started to go down, it quickly got cold. I had another chat with Chris the barman/playwright about Alan Ayckbourn and Bennett – incongruous subjects, admittedly, for this icy location.

During the night, the ship had moved onto the town of Ilulissat, one of the largest towns in Greenland. This was not saying very much, but it certainly looked positively urban compared with anything we had seen in the last week.

After breakfast, we climbed into the Zodiacs and had a dry landing for once. We walked up to the tourist information centre where there was a wide range of quite expensive souvenirs. We then set out for the largest moving glacier in the world. The first part of the hike was along quite a busy road. Although there were only about two or three roads, there were lots of trucks and taxis buzzing past. We passed literally hundreds sled dogs tethered to their posts – their howling was really quite eerie. The road appeared to peter out as we went over a wooden bridge and we then had to hike for two miles over boggy and rocky terrain.

When we arrived, what we saw was absolutely astonishing: the *Jakobshavn Isbrae* (ice fjord), which is the fastest moving glacier in the world and produces a new iceberg every five minutes.

We then took an hour-long Zodiac trip round the emerald green, turquoise and dazzling white icebergs that surrounded Illulissat. I tried to keep a stiff upper lip as we ploughed through what looked like crushed ice.

The ice cracked and crashed around us and we virtually touched one of the bergs. I was slightly tense, bearing in mind that I had seen a glacier split a couple days ago and I had also read that a couple of years ago, an iceberg had broken in two and caused a tidal wave that virtually swamped the town.

One of the more remarkable sights was a waterfall on one side of a particularly large iceberg. Later that day, we had a talk by the ubiquitous Laurie on whaling. This consisted largely of him reading lengthy passages from *Moby Dick* in true preacher style. One of the readings was about a priest who used the skin of a whale's penis as a cassock – not material used daily by the Anglican clergy, I would imagine.

Sadly, our trip finally came to an end with a brisk gale and high seas to send us on our way. It was dangerous to go on deck or the bridge. However, as soon as we turned into the Sondre Stromfjord, we found ourselves in calm waters. This is one of the longest and most stunning fjords in the world and stretches 100 miles inland. We were surrounded by sheer mountains which, given that the channel was quite narrow, loomed over us menacingly.

As a parting gesture, we received a certificate to say that we had crossed the Arctic. Cabin mate Jim of course, complained that this was tacky. Perhaps he should have received a certificate for heroic complaining instead.

The next morning we disembarked at Kangerlussuaq, another remote spot, better known as Bluie West 8. This was the code name for the Sondestrom Air Base, which was built by the Americans during the war as an important stopover for flying missions between the USA and its allies in Europe.

After the war, the airbase was handed back to Denmark, but reverted to the USA during the Korean war. It then became a stopover for SAS flights between Copenhagen and Los Angeles and was now the main international gateway into Greenland, even though it really was miles from anywhere.

The airport was surprisingly comfortable and well equipped but we did have to hang around for quite a while, as the flight back to Ottawa was delayed. I was quite happy to sit back and relax, but some of my American co-passengers reverted to type and began to moan. I heard the words 'let's sue for compensation' wafting over from a dark corner of the departure lounge. Welcome back to the real world.

Chapter 10

Let the Train Take the Strain

As a child, annual visits to my Auntie Eileen and Uncle Eric's house in the Manchester suburb of Didsbury were enormously exciting. Their back garden overlooked the main Midland steam railway from London St Pancras to Manchester Central, now the G-Mex exhibition centre. I always had a timetable to hand, and would check trains for punctuality and destination – but above all I loved the sounds and smells of steam trains.

I recall travelling once with my paternal grandmother who was absolutely tiny and always wore a black straw hat. When we got to St Pancras, she insisted on stopping as we passed the engine, looking up at the driver who towered above her and thanking him for the smooth ride.

Thus I felt that I was revisiting my youth as I reported for duty at the Minehead terminus of the West Somerset Railway one blustery August morning. I had only ever stood on the footplate of a steam engine in railway museums, and found it hard to believe that today I was going to be part of a real passenger-carrying crew.

In reality, it takes several years of hard, and often dirty, graft to qualify as a steam train driver or fireman but the West Somerset, along with several other heritage railways throughout the UK, run courses for enthusiasts to learn the fundamentals of preparing, firing and driving locomotives. You need to be tolerably fit, as you will be expected to clamber in and out of the cab, which in itself can be quite a feat, shovel coal, duck between the engine and the carriages in order to couple and uncouple and generally buzz around being useful.

Courses tend to run in the autumn and winter when the passenger services are suspended, because you are not allowed to drive a train with passengers aboard until you are properly qualified.

Depending on your choice, you will learn how to prepare a locomotive, the principles of working a steam locomotive, signalling, braking, safety, driving and firing. Guided by a West Somerset Railway instructor, you will haul a train of empty coaches or freight wagons along part of the line. You can start with a half-day practical introduction to the mysteries of the steam engine on the Bishop Lydeard to Norton Fitzwarren section. You will experience using the regulator and firing the locomotive, but you won't tow any coaches or wagons.

However the serious stuff starts with a two-day course, which has theoretical and practical elements. Numbers are limited to a maximum of six participants to ensure each gets as much experience as possible.

The course involves talks and demonstrations on safety, making steam, locomotive operation and signalling, and includes visits to the locomotive workshop and signal box. This is followed by practical lessons in preparing the locomotive and ends with three return trips between Minehead and Blue Anchor hauling an empty passenger train. You spend one trip firing and the other driving. While others have their turn on the footplate, you travel on the train with the guard.

After you have completed the first course, you can take a more advanced day course, which gives more practical experience, again with a maximum of five other participants. After preparing your locomotive, you then haul a freight train from Minehead to Williton and back, driving one way and firing the other.

There are two further courses. One is another day-long course which gives more practical driving experience. A fourth and final course entails two full round- trips from Minehead to Bishops Lydeard (or vice versa), hauling empty coaches to a normal working timetable.

Because there were no courses being run when I was able to get to Minehead, the management of the WSR agreed, with a bit of special pleading, that I could spend the day on the footplate of a 1925 former Somerset and Dorset Joint Railway '7F' 2-8-0, N88.

However, they emphasised that the controls would be strictly out of bounds while the train was actually carrying paying passengers, although I could shovel coal and try and make myself useful on the footplate.

For readers with an interest in these things, this engine had its origins as far back as the beginning of the First World War, when two batches of SDJR 2-8-0 mineral engines were built to the design of Henry Fowler in the Midland Railway workshops at Derby. Construction began in 1913 and they cost £3,500 each.

To be even more technical, the locomotives were the first on the Somerset and Dorset to have outside cylinders and Walschaerts valve gears. They were too long to be turned on the S&D turntables, so were provided with tender cabs.

The locomotives were amongst the most powerful in the country at the time. The design allowed for the steep gradients and tight curves of the Bath Extension. Three brake cylinders were used; two operated on the front faces of the three rearward pairs of coupled wheels, whilst the third cylinder actuated brake blocks on the rear faces of the front coupled pair and the clasp brakes on the pony truck. Sand was held in six sand boxes, and was steam operated.

My engine was one of a second batch, delivered in 1925. They were built by Robert Stevenson & Co. Ltd at a cost of £6,570 – an indication that inflation is nothing new. The second batch had larger boilers than the first and were slightly shorter but two tons heavier, giving greater adhesion, and were driven from the left. At the end of the steam era it was sold as scrap, but was rescued in 1968 by the members of the Somerset and Dorset Railway Circle who bought it on the 'never never' for £2,500.

After a somewhat chequered period, restoration finally brought the engine back to pristine condition about ten years ago and it is now on a 20-year full repairing lease to the West Somerset Railway.

Having done my homework prior to my visit, I was aware that this particular type of engine had not been without its mishaps over the years, as I had found this description of a 1936 incident on the S&DR website.

This incident could easily have been written for an old Ealing Comedy Film. On the 29th of July 1936, an up freight train hauled by a 2-8-0 locomotive, had just passed signals at danger in the vicinity of Writhlington signal box, near Radstock. It came into slight collision with 0-6-0T locomotive No.7620, which was engaged in shunting duties at Braysdown Colliery.

The crew of the 2-8-0 engine had jumped off in anticipation of the collision. The driver of the 0-6-0T, also realising what was about to happen, started to reverse his train and leapt off, his fireman did the same, leaving the regulator slightly open. The driver then managed to clamber aboard the now almost stationary 2-8-0 and brought it to a halt.

The 0-6-0T rolled off towards Bath, minus its crew, propelling a rake of 8 wagons in front of it at ever increasing speed on the undulating gradients. By the time the runaway train reached Midford, some 5 miles away, most of the wagons had been pushed off the track on the sharp curves, causing considerable damage and partially wrecking the signal box and station buildings at Midford. Fortunately the eventual derailment of the last wagon brought the engine to a stand before it could foul the junction at Bath.

I kept my fingers crossed that I wouldn't be required to 'jump off in anticipation of a collision', although my driver, Dereck, and fireman, Roger, looked far too competent to get into such a situation. Virtually all the drivers and fireman on heritage railways these days have other daytime jobs or are retired. There are few original ex-British Rail staff around, as the last passenger and freight steam trains were withdrawn around forty years ago.

Dereck made jam for a living, which he supplied to tourist shops and hotels around Somerset, while Roger was a retired truck driver and garage owner. Both obviously had enormous love and enthusiasm for their job, although Roger did have a bit of moan when we were a few minutes late leaving Minehead, because some last-minute passengers were holding things up. Despite this, he waved majestically at the many holidaymakers who watched as we sped by, and was only too happy to lift young kids onto the footplate during a break at Bishop Lydeard before our return journey.

I had never been to Minehead before, and had visions of one big

Butlin's holiday camp. Despite the slightly nerve-wracking drive along the narrow and twisty A39 from Bridgewater, the town came as a pleasant surprise. Admittedly Butlins somewhat dominates the seafront with a building that looked rather like the Millennium Dome, but the town centre and the delightful harbour have none of the tackiness so often found in seaside resorts.

It was the splendidly named Sir Peregrine Fuller Palmer Acland Bt, who called and chaired a meeting at the Egremont Hotel at Williton, near Minehead, Somerset, on Wednesday 9 July 1856 with a view to promoting the building of a railway from Watchet to connect with the expanding Great Western Railway at Norton Junction near to Taunton. Sadly for Sir Peregrine, his wife and three children all died of TB, but at least the railway has survived as a monument to his endeavours.

Sir Peregrine had prepared well for the meeting, and arranged the attendance of the great Isambard Kingdom Brunel who spoke in favour of a railway, both in commercial and engineering terms. Brunel, who had clearly looked over the possible routes, favoured a line from Watchet or Porlock to Bridgwater.

In the event, the meeting led to the formation of the first West Somerset Railway Company, and later to the building and opening of the line from the Bristol and Exeter Railway at Norton Junction, just west of Taunton, to the harbour town of Watchet. The chairman announced that Watchet would be the terminus, and it seems that Brunel's proposal was then agreed upon.

A prospectus was issued by the new company, with Sir Peregrine in the chair and Isambard Kingdom Brunel as engineer. However, the hoped-for flood of subscriptions failed to appear but work went ahead nonetheless and construction began on 10 April 1859. The first stretch of the line opened in 1862 and was extended 14 years later to Minehead.

It was one of the last lines to receive the Beeching axe in 1971 but eight years later it was operational again as a heritage railway. However a crucial link between the main line and Bishops Lydeard had been cut, and it was only recently that this link was restored so that excursion trains could now come again from all over the national rail network.

Although the first train of the day didn't leave Minehead until

1015, I had been told to report for duty at 0730. This seemed rather early, particularly as the hosts of my bed and breakfast refused to serve breakfast before 0800 – surely another opportunity for Polish enterpreneurs?

I was kitted out with overalls and an old British Rail fireman's cap, and then introduced to Dereck and Roger who were already hard at work. It didn't take me long to realise how long it takes to prepare an engine for service. Dereck, as driver, was in charge of the engine, but he and Roger worked as a close-knit team to carry out the extensive preparation required before we could pull out of the quarter-mile long platform at Minehead.

Steam engines are relatively simple in principle, but moody and sometimes difficult in practice. A railway engine contains a coal-burning furnace, which heats water contained in a large boiler to produce steam. The accumulated pressure from the expanding vapour drives the pistons of the engine, enabling the train to move forward or backwards.

The principal duty of the fireman is to keep a bright and even fire roaring, and ensure that the water in the boiler is at the exact level needed to maintain speed across different types of terrain, such as flat beds, hills and curves. A bad fire can result in either low water or low steam levels, leading to unscheduled stops and slow running times.

Learning how to properly 'fire' a steam engine would appear to be a true craft. I found it hard enough trying to stand on the sliding cab of the train, but maintaining an even fire and taking accurate readings of the water glass under these conditions takes a lot of skill. A fireman really has to know his track like the back of his hand, so that he can adjust steam pressure according to the gradient and curves.

Roger's first duty that morning was to examine and test the water gauge in order to check the boiler water levels. He then had to make up the fire, but before doing this, he had to ensure that the ashpan was properly cleared of ashes and that the ashpan dampers were in working order. He then had to open and inspect the smoke box and see that it was cleared of ashes and then shut the smoke box door tightly. This was very important: because if there was an air leak, it would be hard to keep up the steam pressure which gives the engine its power.

Roger's understanding of his boiler seemed as much of an art as a science, and throughout the return journey he endeavoured to shovel the Russian coal evenly inside the boiler to get up the maximum head of steam.

As I understand it, the art of firing is to obtain the maximum amount of heat from every pound of coal fired. Thus Roger had to anticipate the engine's requirements and manage the fire and injectors accordingly, so that steam was available for gradients, but not wasted when standing or running down hills. My first job was to shovel coal, but being left-handed, I found it hard to get the smooth action required. Because the engine was driven on the left, I had to shovel from the right side in order not to get in Dereck's way. For a left-hander, it felt extremely unnatural, although I daresay I would have learned in time.

In the meantime, Dereck was busy lubricating all the moving parts of the engine, which was his sole responsibility and which he did in a very methodical fashion. He also washed the entire engine with great pride.

The loading of coal and water then had to be supervised, and when everything seemed in order, we shunted the engine to the front of the train and hitched it to the brown and cream carriages which were by now full of passengers.

With a blow of the whistle, we eventually pulled out of Minehead. The first stretch to Dunster was level with some lovely coastal views, provided you ignored Butlins and the local sewage treatment plant. I thought Dunster station looked vaguely familiar and subsequently found out that it was the prototype for the Hornby model railway station I had as a child.

From Dunster, we steamed further along the coast to Blue Anchor, which seemed mainly to consist of caravans and mobile homes. I was intrigued by one of the few remaining traditional level crossings with the gates controlled by a wheel in the signal box.

During the 1930s, the the Great Western Railway, which by now ran the West Somerset Railway, upgraded the single track to double track between Norton Fitzwarren and Bishops Lydeard and Dunster and Minehead. However as the line was being run down during the Beeching era, the second track was ripped up.

Single-track working, as I discovered, involved some fairly

complicated manoeuvres. I must confess that I didn't really understand all the intricacies, but from Minehead to Blue Anchor, we were given two differently coloured electric key tokens, which were swapped at Dunster. These tokens indeed looked like large keys and were designed to prevent two trains accidentally travelling on the same line in opposite directions.

From Blue Anchor, we started to swing inland and climb up to Washford. As we did so, Roger gave me some more training in shovelling coal, although I could tell by his pained look that my skills in this direction were severely challenged. The Somerset and Dorset Railway Trust has a small museum at Washford Station but I didn't have time to jump off and have a look around. Instead we started our descent to the coast at Watchet, which was the original railway terminus.

Wachet used to be one of the busiest harbours on the Bristol Channel with railway sidings by the quay, where esparto grass was imported from Spain and taken to the local paper mill. As we left Watchet, the railway line clung close to the cliff tops. For many years, there was concern that erosion would destroy the line at this point, but it had been shored up by several loads of boulders at the foot of the cliffs. I could see across to South Wales and the uninhabited island of Steep Holme, an important bird sanctuary.

From Watchet, we steamed on to Williton and climbed onto Woolston Moor until we reached the oddly named Stogumber and then onto Crowcombe Heathfield. Our engine wasn't pulling entirely to Roger's satisfaction, so I rather hoped he wouldn't blame it on my shovelling coal into the wrong parts of the boiler.

We then started our three-and-a-half-mile descent from the Quantocks, twisting and turning as we followed the river valley down to the end of the first part of our journey at Bishops Lydeard. Dereck shunted the engine to the other end of the train for our return journey, Roger topped up the water tank and I climbed onto the top of the tender to shovel coal down to make it easier to shift into the boiler. Roger and Dereck then lifted eager-faced children onto the footplate for a quick look before we set off back to Minehead.

After the last passengers had been disgorged, Dereck and Roger handed over the engine to the next crew and, reluctantly, I took off my overalls, washed the soot off my hands and said my farewells.

On my way back to London, I stopped at a motorway service station and wondered why everyone was staring at me. Then I got a glance at myself in the mirror in the gents' toilet. My face was entirely covered in soot which I had failed to wash off in my haste to say goodbye to Dereck and Roger, who had obviously been too polite to comment. I washed off the last traces of my day on the footplate, and promised myself that I would book myself onto the next available course, as soon as I could find the time.

Chapter 11

Sailing into the Sunset

The minute I met Skip and Steve I knew I was in for an energetic week. The two mates from Wolverhampton appeared to be pumped up on adrenaline and testosterone, and their consumption of the local Greek beer with ouzo chasers further fuelled their enthusiasm.

The island of Lefkas is one of the Ionian Islands, which trace a ragged line down the west coast of Greece. Tourism grinds to a halt in this neck of the woods at the beginning of October, when the summer months of hot sunshine give way to a more changeable climate, with spectacular storms and heavy rain.

Thus, on a late September Sunday night, it was dark and deserted when our bus pulled in at the somewhat rickety jetty at the far end of Nidri, Lefkas's tourist hot spot. **Sunvil Sailing**, which organised the trip, offer learn-to-sail holidays and flotilla cruises with live-aboard accommodation, where those who normally lead a sedentary and perhaps somewhat isolated life, can hurl themselves round a small sailing boat for week or two in (very) close proximity to family, friends or a bunch of strangers.

Sunvil's sailing operations holidays are run from the unremarkable *Hotel Armonia*. Compared with the neighbouring (and rather smarter) **Neilson**'s, which has a whole marina of shining boats and a large hotel base of its own just up the road, **Sunvil**'s sailing package seemed a slightly idiosyncratic and homespun operation.

At the beginning and end of the season, the company runs 'Pot Luck' cruises, which cater for singles and couples sharing a yacht with other sailors. I joined one of the tuition yachts called *Artimis*, named after the Greek goddess of chastity.

My 'pot luck' turned out to be Skip and Steve, as well as a gentle and delightful national newspaper sub-editor called Chris and Bernd, our very smooth German skipper, who had forsaken the well-paid world of marketing for the paltry £150 a week plus tips he earned trying to teach us how to sail.

Words take on a fresh meaning when you are talking about sailing boats. My 'cabin' was a cupboard in the bows of the boat, a French-built Gibsea 35. The 'heads' was a small toilet with a complicated pumping system which gave up the ghost at one point until the imperturbable Bernd put on his rubber gloves, removed his sunglasses and managed to get things moving again – literally!

There were three tuition yachts in the flotilla, with another four sailed by families and friends with reasonable nautical knowledge. The three skippers were a mixed bunch including the aforementioned Bernd, Nick, a former paratrooper with a head the shape of a rugby ball, and Pete, who was a former jockey and professional showjumper.

The crew on one of the other teaching boats consisted of a garage owner and his two twenty-something kids with a serious addiction to roll ups (of the purely tobacco variety one assumes), and a forty year old divorcee who was still angry with her ex for running off with a young Byellorussian bride.

Each day we were given a short briefing on our destination port for that evening and a weather forecast. Then we went shopping for lunch, which usually consisted of tomatoes, bread, cheese, yoghurt and fruit – healthy, but slightly monotonous. The daily pattern was to set sail at about 1030 and then anchor in a friendly-looking bay for a leisurely lunch at about 1330.

Because most of the ports were crowded, largely unsupervised and with limited moorings and pontoons, the earlier you got into harbour, the better the berth you were able to grab. Because hyperactive Steve and Skip demanded the maximum amount of sailing, we were always last in and spent quite a bit of time each evening trying to find somewhere to drop anchor.

As we only had a basic gang plank to connect us with the shore, we often had to make death-defying leaps onto the jetty. While British health and safety *gauleiters* would have had apoplectic fits if they could have seen us, no one came to any harm, despite the beer and ouzo chasers that were consumed before we went ashore for dinner. On a serious note, however, this kind of activity is not suitable for those who are not reasonably agile and you certainly need good sea legs. In other words, if you get seasick on a cross-channel ferry, this is not the holiday for you. Nonetheless our skipper was always mindful of the fact that I had only just recovered from a heart attack, and always made sure that the Wolverhampton Wanderers got the hardest tasks!

The skippers arranged for all the flotilla sailors to have dinner together each evening which gave us a chance to talk to other people and swap our sailing experiences. While I like Greek food, in general the restaurants were pretty mediocre and the food was invariably lukewarm. It also tended to be quite fatty, so warnings about heart-friendly diets left me contemplating nothing more than a dressing-free salad on more than one occasion.

The local wine was also a bit suspect, but after a few glasses you tended not to notice any more. Prices in Greece have risen steeply since it joined the Euro, and an average meal cost me around €25.

Local entrepreneurs offered hot showers in all the ports for €2–4. However no soap or towels were provided, and you were expected to mop the floor when you'd finished. But they were always clean and the water was generally hot. Only Skip complained because he thought that free showers should be provided as an EU benefit.

Bernd was a great skipper and an excellent teacher, and he exercised enormous patience and tact in dealing with his disparate crew of divorced, middle-aged men. He indulged Skip and Steve's belief in their nautical prowess while teaching Chris and myself some of the basic sailing knowledge we sadly lacked. Knots were my great downfall – I have a blind spot when it comes to tying even a shoelace – but I enjoyed taking the wheel and learning to become a passably useful member of the crew.

The Ionian Islands are spectacularly beautiful and we sailed to Kefalonia (as in *Captain Corelli's Mandolin*), Ithaca and the charming little island of Kalamos, which has a handful of shops and restaurants and – improbably – a 24-hour disco. This is Greece as one imagines it 50 years ago, and it is apparently virtually empty of tourists in the winter.

I am not sure I would have wanted to spend much more time

with the Wolverhampton Wanderers or eating lukewarm food, and it was all a bit rough and ready: more youth hostel than luxury hotel; more *Swallows and Amazons* than luxury yachting. But it was well organised, the tuition was excellent and my fellow crewmembers were kind-hearted and caring, if a little over enthusiastic.

Chapter 12

Digging Down Under

Australia makes it so difficult for Brits to get working visas that most people are surprised to know that the Queen is still technically Head of State. Furthermore, its National Parks are Crown land which means, in theory, that Her Majesty has a stake in large slabs of Oz's vast terrain.

She has probably never heard, however, of Kwiambal National Park which is located in a remote corner of Northern New South Wales and is named after an aboriginal tribe that used to live there. It is a singularly remote and little visited spot, some 20 miles along a dirt road from the nearest town called Ashford, with a population of 500.

Myself and nine other volunteers had arrived there after a six-hour drive from Brisbane in a bumpy, battered Toyota minibus. We had all signed up to work for a month with **Conservation Volunteers Australia**, which operates similar programmes to those in which I had previously taken part in the UK with the National Trust and British Trust for Conservation Volunteers. Although I had booked this trip through an outfit called **Gap Year for Grownups**, all the other participants were young enough to be my kids and despite the fact that the programme was open to Australians, the majority of the volunteers came from Europe, Korea and Japan – a mix that had little obvious logic but generally worked quite well.

After a week mainly clearing non-native plants from parks around Brisbane, we had been told we would be moving to Gladstone, an industrial town in Northern Queensland. However, at the last moment, we were diverted to Kwiambal, several hundred miles south of our original destination. We were told that we would spend the next two weeks building a two-and-a-half mile walking trail though the park, and that we would be accommodated in a ranger's hut. We were also warned that it would be very cold at night and that there would be limited facilities.

Not only were we volunteers, but we had actually paid several hundred pounds for the privilege of preserving the environment for a variety of endangered species, including koalas, large bent wing bats, turquoise parrots, glossy black cockatoos, paled headed snakes and Murray turtles.

The journey from Brisbane was long and hot, and when we arrived at Ashford, it was obvious that we were going to be a long way from civilisation for the next two weeks. Even though it proudly announced that it had a 50 kph speed limit, the town only had one main street with very little through traffic and had the look and feel of one of those Australian films set in the 1950s.

There was one general store which was large and cool but had very little stock, as well as a small bakery, a petrol station, a hardware store and − incongruously − a gift shop called *Old Fart's Arts and Crafts*.

The general store seemed to being doing little business, which was hardly surprising, given its near-empty shelves and ageing stock. My digital camera had just ended up on the Great Barrier Reef so I asked the lady on the till, without much expectation, whether she stocked throw-away cameras. Much to my surprise, she pulled two down from a dusty shelf.

"There've been a run on these," she said. "We've sold two since Easter. Mind you, we're trying to sell the shop, so we won't be getting any more."

As the former owner of a village shop in the Yorkshire Dales, a wave of nostalgia overtook me. Just for a moment, I imagined myself as the proprietor of the *Ashford General Stores*, until I remembered the long hours for pitiful returns. On the other hand, there were 500 local inhabitants with nowhere else to shop, as well as around 8,000 visitors to Kwiambal every year. The nearest town of any size was Inverell, which was a two-hour round trip by truck.

The owner told me that she used to live on the Gold Coast (a sort of Blackpool-type strip along the south east coast of Queensland), but had moved to Ashford six years ago. Unfortunately her husband had recently suffered from a stroke and the nearest doctor was 40 miles away.

I am not sure I entirely believed this story, as the lady who ran *Old Fart's Arts and Crafts* told me that her husband and the grocery owner's spouse had gone off bushwalking for two days.

The Old Farter (if she will forgive this label) had come to Ashford from Sydney's western suburbs five years previously, and had brought 11 members of her family with her. I had often noticed that, whenever I was in Sydney, I only saw young and beautiful people. When I asked a young (and beautiful) Sydneysider where all the oldies had gone, she said they were clustered together in the dreary western suburbs, well out of sight of her and her contemporaries.

This lady had obviously decided that she was not going to rot away, and had made a new life for herself and her family in this strange little town.

I then went into the bakery where there was great excitement because a local schoolgirl had been chosen to sing the national anthem before the Australia v New Zealand rugby league test match. "Just fancy," said the baker, "one of our girls on the telly. Nothing like that has ever happened in Ashford".

He then told me that he was an amateur flying ace and had recently flown a vintage plane at the Biggin Hill International Air Show in Kent. When I said that Biggin Hill was not too far from Ashford, Kent, there was great excitement which led to a discussion about the Channel Tunnel and the fact that when he went on the Eurostar to Paris, he couldn't believe that the train went so fast that he couldn't read the station names.

Having once taken 23 hours to travel the 900-odd miles between Adelaide and Sydney on the *Indian Pacific* railway – an average of roughly 39mph – I understood his surprise that trains could go so fast. We then had a chat about the difference between Ashford Kent and Ashford NSW. This was something I was well equipped for as I had started my career as a newspaper reporter in an office over a fish shop in Ashford Kent. I was then persuaded to buy one of his special cheese and bacon pies as a gesture of international goodwill. However, it sat on my stomach like a lead weight for the rest of the day.

Returning to the general store, I found my fellow volunteers trying to find something to buy. The owner looked at our motley crew with barely disguised curiosity, and asked me who we were and what we were doing in Ashford.

I doubt that Ashford had seen such a mixed bunch before. Our group consisted of myself; three Koreans called Sue-Jung, Nam-Pyo and Eui-Ho who had conveniently adopted the European names of Jack, Leo and Ellie in order to make our lives easier; Jen, a very loud and skinny American girl with the most penetrating voice I had ever encountered; Sue, an 18 year old teenager from Kendal who only seemed to have booze and sex on her mind; Josh, a half-English, half-Sri Lankan public school boy with a permanently shaking hand, a serious smoking habit and an infantile sense of humour; a charming 20 year-old Belgian lad called René; and Des our infinitely patient and rugged leader.

The moment I met Jen, I knew I was going to hate her. First of all, her voice had the same effect as a dentist's drill and she never stopped talking about her Mom, Pop, life in San Diego and her very responsible role as captain of her local paintball spraying team.

The two Korean boys had just completed their national service, while Ellie acted as mother figure to her two male compatriots and cooked special Korean meals for them with ingredients they had managed to buy in Brisbane before our departure.

Despite his slightly taciturn nature, Des was an interesting and kind guy who boasted Cornish aristocratic descent. He was very interested in astrology, but sadly never fulfilled his promise to read my stars.

We eventually set off along the 20 mile unmade road to Kwiambal, and after a bone-shaking 45 minutes, we arrived at what looked like a suburban bungalow dumped in the middle of nowhere. Why on earth had someone thought to put this Wimpy-style house, more Luton cul-de-sac than outback Oz, in a national park? I had visions of some exiled Pom deciding that a nice bit of coving, a wool carpet and a bottom-of-the-range Homebase kitchen would be just right in this outback setting.

The only problem with this suburban home-from-home was that the builders had walked (or in this case driven) off the job halfway through renovations, and thus the place was a building site, although there was at least one bathroom that functioned reasonably most of the time. Fergus, the 29 year-old park ranger, had not thought to organise pillows or blankets, although there were enough beds. The only furniture consisted of an elderly sofa and some tatty office chairs and desks, while the cooker was old and hazardous and the washing machine leaked. Otherwise, perfection!

Volunteers can adapt to anything, supposedly, so we settled down to fight for our own little bit of space. The girls managed to grab the only room with electric heating, while the rest of us looked forward to freezing nights with nothing but lightweight sleeping bags to fight off the chill. For the first time in my life, I actually woke up in the night with my teeth chattering and ended up sleeping in a tracksuit with two t-shirts, gloves, socks and a bobble hat! An SOS to the regional office of the national park eventually yielded some grubby fire blankets a couple of days later.

The compensation for this discomfort was a succession of beautifully warm days when the thermometer stayed at a pleasant 23°C from dawn to dusk. Furthermore, the scenery was the most spectacular I had encountered for a long time. Kwiambal really was a beautiful, yet virtually undiscovered spot.

Kwiambal and the Ashford area had been a large tobacco growing area from the 1800s until the end of the First World War, when prices slumped. Production resumed in 1969 and it was grown and dried in the area of the national park itself until 1994. Given that most of our party were heavy smokers, it seemed a pity that they couldn't just nip down the road and hand pick their own roll-ups.

Until 2000, locals were pretty well free to do what they wanted with the land, but at that point, the **New South Wales National Parks & Wildlife Service** acquired the land. The locals felt robbed, and had taken to petty vandalism, as well as illegal fishing and hunting, as a way of protesting against unwelcome state intervention.

Although the park service had made much of its concern for the area's aboriginal heritage, its approach seemed typically heavy-handed, bureaucratic and designed to antagonise.

In its draft management plan for the area, it wrote:

Aboriginal people with a connection to the park, will be permitted to carry out activities in the park related to the maintenance of traditional links to the country. Any such activities must comply with the objectives and policies of this plan of management, the NPW Act and Regulations and have minimal environmental impact.

The work we had to do was quite varied. Some of it was pretty hard, particularly cutting up logs and branches to clear a trail. The most tedious part was raking away leaves and debris in order to establish a well-defined path. We also had to install way marks, which involved digging deep holes in very hard ground with fairly rudimentary tools.

Digging put pressure on my shoulders, which felt as if someone was pushing all his weight down on me from above. Raking was also hard on the stomach muscles and after three or four days, I found myself walking with a curious gait, and was forced to avoid bending over as much as possible.

Australia has an amazing quantity of spiders, snakes and other creepy crawlies, which are just waiting to take a bite out of you. Thus the most important thing was to watch where you were walking and to lift up stones carefully to ensure you didn't disturb an ant's nest or some irritable creature.

The two Korean boys worked extremely hard, while Ellie proceeded at a somewhat leisurely pace. The English contingent, on the other hand, disappeared at regular intervals. Sue spent a lot of time motionless, standing by Fergus's side, looking longingly into his eyes. Josh seemed permanently anxious that there would be insufficient food, and was often found rummaging through the cool box to check that there were enough sandwiches and cakes for his lunch. He was also forever losing things and spent a considerable amount of time wondering back and forth, looking for his water bottle, iPod and tobacco.

Despite this, we actually got a surprising amount of work done and at the end of the first week we had completed the trail. Despite several aching muscles and a few insect bites, I was delighted to have survived thus far in good health – particularly as I celebrated the first anniversary of my heart attack halfway through the week.

Although we were due to stay two weeks in Kwiambal, our plans, as usual, were changed at the last minute. Thus, after a week, we moved on to Bald Rock National Park, halfway back to Brisbane.

Bald Rock itself is the largest granite rock in Australia and is 750 metres long, 500 metres wide and 200 metres high.

The park was located near a small town called Tenterfield, which not only had a mobile phone signal, but also a small internet café – urban sophistication at last! While a fairly insignificant looking place, Tenterfield had an important role in Australian history and was known as the *Birthplace of Our Nation*, because Sir Henry Parkes delivered his famous federation speech in the Tenterfield School of Arts on 24 October 1889. This ultimately led to the formation of Australia as a single country on New Year's Day 1901.

The minute we arrived in Tenterfield there was an excited babble of Korean, French and English voices, as everyone realised that they could actually use their mobile phones for the first time in ten days. There was also a dash for the internet café, although everyone's enthusiasm for checking their emails was tempered by the painfully slow and expensive connection.

Tenterfield had a population of a mere 4,000, but it seemed like a buzzing metropolis after the remoteness of Kwiambal and Ashford. I offered to help Des with the shopping in the rather scruffy Bi-Lo supermarket, which had the advantage of being cheap and reasonably cheerful. This was important as our food budget was very limited and the Koreans, in particular, had phenomenal appetites.

In fact food in general was something of an issue. The Koreans were desperate for rice, garlic and a black soya paste, which seemed to be a vital ingredient in their cooking. Jack seemed to suffer from acute hunger and demanded food with so much spice and chilli peppers, that he invariably got a stomach ache and was promptly sick.

He turned up his nose at Australian 'tucker' and demanded that Ellie should cook him Korean food, while the rest of us ate whatever we found that wasn't too expensive. Jack's English was very limited but he constantly muttered "must have Korean food, very hungry and Australian food no good" like a mantra. He also seemed to sleep whenever he wasn't eating or working.

Luckily for him, Ellie was very good-natured and mothered him endlessly. She started cooking at all times of the day and night in order to satisfy his unpredictable appetite. The fact that the rest of us had eaten, washed up and settled down for the evening, seemed quite immaterial.

Jack would then eat rapidly and prodigiously, always adding raw chillies. He would then sweat and clutch his stomach while Ellie and Leo beat his back vigorously, which appeared to be a Korean cure for stomach aches.

Having loaded the shopping into the minibus in Tenterfield, we discovered that Josh had disappeared. As far as we could make out from a phone conversation he had had earlier with his doctor in London, he needed some urgent medication and had been told to go to the local 'travel clinic'. I gathered that this doctor was based in Harley Street and perhaps didn't appreciate that Tenterfield was not exactly lined with such places.

On the other hand, for £20 or so, most Australian doctors would write you a prescription if the drug was available locally, but that was probably too simple a concept for Josh to grasp, even though we had told him this at least half a dozen times.

So he had set off in search of this elusive clinic. The kindly René had gone with him, perhaps realising that Josh was almost certainly going to lose the plot (not to mention himself) in one way or another. Nonetheless, Des began to get quite rattled when neither returned after an hour and a half, and it was beginning to get dark.

Apart from the fact that we were getting cold and fed up hanging around, Des was also aware that we had to get to a ranger's hut in the nearby oddly named Boonoo Boonoo National Park. Pronounced 'bunna bunoo', it was a local Aboriginal term for big rocks, but big rocks or not, we only had quite vague instructions as to how to find our accommodation. Driving after dark was not a great idea anyway as the area was overrun with kangaroos, which were likely to leap out in front of our headlights.

As you can imagine, a collision between a car and kangaroo is likely to kill the kangaroo and damage the car, particularly as roos are easily blinded by headlights or startled by engine noise, and in mid-bound, can reach speeds of 30mph.

Two hours later – with Josh and René still nowhere to be seen – Des was fuming, everyone else was grumbling and it was totally dark. Then suddenly, from nowhere, the two came ambling into the car park and gave us a friendly wave. It was the only time I saw Des lose his temper, but we never got an explanation as to where they had been. Worse still, it was clear that Josh had not got his pills. In desperation Des dragged him to a local doctor the following day, where a prescription was immediately dispensed and the drug purchased without any problem.

We didn't have a set of roo bars so we were lucky to find the ranger's hut in the dark without any incident. If we had hit a kangaroo, it would have been our responsibility to finish the poor marsupial off and then take its corpse to the nearest vet.

On arrival, it was immediately clear that the ranger's hut was far too small for us, but we managed to sort ourselves into a somewhat disorganised clutter. I ended up on a mattress on the floor, surrounded by a collection of bags I had collected on my travels. In fact I felt a bit like one of the street dwellers I used to see on the pavements when I worked opposite the Savoy Hotel in London.

I was feeling slightly sombre anyway, as I had heard on the car radio that one of Australia's best-known television reporters, Richard Carleton, had dropped dead of a heart attack at the age of 62, while reporting the rescue of two workers from a collapsed mine in Tasmania – an incident which had gripped the nation for several days.

Although I had, by now, got over the fear that another heart attack might be just round the corner, I still got a jolt every time I heard of someone dying from heart problems of one sort or another.

However, I put these thoughts behind me as I tried to sleep in temperatures that had again dropped to freezing, despite the fact that it had been 24°C just before sunset. Eventually I drifted off, trying to ignore the snoring and smelly feet of my colleagues who had arranged themselves horizontally around me.

The next morning, Fergus, who had rearranged his duties so that he could be in attendance on the doe-eyed Sue, turned up and announced that he had no idea what we were supposed to be doing, so that we might as well climb Bald Rock, some 260 metres above a landscape of rocky outcrops.

On the way to the foot of Bald Rock, I heard on the radio that that a 31 year-old Malaysian man had just married a lady of 104, and that he was her twenty-first husband. It occurred to me that if I lived until I was 104 I would still have 46 years to go, and that if I was to match this lusty centenarian's record, I would have to marry and divorce a different woman every two years for the rest of my life.

Thoughts of longevity started me wondering whether I might be pushing my heart too hard now, particularly as I had also pulled a hamstring a few days before. Nonetheless, I decided that as the whole point of this trip was to test out what I was able to do, I would follow the others to the top.

I was determined not to be left behind and found, much to my surprise, that I climbed the rock pretty easily, although I did have to catch my breath on a couple of occasions.

Luckily, it was a beautiful day – as it had been for most of my trip – but quite cool, as we were about 4,000 feet above sea level. When I got to the top, I was rewarded with a great view over Queensland and the Richmond Range.

Sue and Jen, the loud American, had followed Fergus to the top with no apparent trouble but as we lay in the sun, Sue started to groan and made some very extravagant and dramatic gestures. Jen cradled her in her arms and Fergus leant over her with great concern. She muttered in a husky voice that she felt ill and could not possibly get to the foot of the rock without some manly assistance.

It was probably just as well that Fergus did not see the look of total incredulity on the faces of the rest of us, as he gave Sue a fireman's lift and proceeded to clamber down a virtually sheer slope, which was only deemed fit for experienced climbers.

The rest of us descended the way we had come and found that by the time we had got back to the car park, Sue and Fergus had snuggled down in the back of his truck, with Jen in the front, looking like a frustrated chaperone. In the meantime, Des thought that the rest of us had better actually do some work, so we started clearing some weeds and hanging branches in a slightly desultory way. Sue inevitably recovered from her terrible affliction within half an hour, but announced that she was too exhausted to do any more work that day.

To make matters worse, Josh had managed to lose the drugs that had just been painstakingly acquired for him, and at this point, Des decided he had had enough, and disappeared into the bush for a couple of hours. This upset the Koreans who thought something terrible had happened to him and decided to go searching.

I tried to explain to them that he just wanted some peace and quiet, but clearly this was not a concept they easily understood, and the three of them set off to look for him. This left René and me (as

Sue and Jen were still ensconced with Fergus in his truck and Josh was fast asleep on a rock), to carry out a bit of work, although by this stage, our enthusiasm was beginning to wear thin too.

However, as predicted, Des returned, the Koreans emerged from the undergrowth puzzled but clearly relieved that our leader was in one piece, and we all agreed that we might as well call it a day and return to our cluttered warren.

On our return, Sue immediately threw herself onto a mattress on the floor, clutching her head and started to make gruesome moaning noises. However the rest of the party decided they had had enough of her dramatics and simply stepped over her. Even Fergus looked slightly hounded.

After this, we all settled down for the next few days and managed to achieve a reasonable amount, particularly some fencing in an area that needed re-seeding. On the last night, even Sue and Jen managed to re-engage with the rest of the world and we had a large and quite jolly barbecue.

On balance, despite everything, we had achieved a lot over the previous two weeks, and I had enjoyed the physical challenges. However, I was not unhappy to be returning to Brisbane.

I cadged a bed for a couple of nights from my cousin Ed, who had recently returned to Brisbane after 15 years in Manchester where the cold and damp had finally got to him. Two days of calm, decent food and civilised company restored my spirits and I felt ready for my next assignment in Noosa National Park, some hundred miles north of Brisbane on Queensland's Sunshine Coast.

My new colleagues were quite different. There was an even larger contingent of Koreans, but they were slightly older and much calmer than the previous group. There was also a very laid back French girl in her mid-thirties and a delightful Japanese trainee teacher. Unlike the previous group, they were mature and we all bonded very well.

This time there was no hostel – just a couple of tents and a makeshift tarpaulin. I decided that this really was more than I could stand, and opted for a very cheap and pleasant holiday 'unit' about ten minutes' walk away from the municipal camp site where the other volunteers were staying. This turned out to be the best £125 I had spent in a long time. For the first time in nearly a month, I had some space of my own and a bit of privacy.

By now, I assumed that there would almost certainly be another change of plan. Sure enough, while I was helping my fellow volunteers to put up their tents, Des received a phone call from the Ranger from the Queensland National Park, saying that we were going to work in Mudjimba, some 50 miles back towards Brisbane.

It would probably have been sensible to give up on camping in Noosa and find somewhere nearer the work site, but for a number of reasons (including the fact that I was now ensconced in a flat and had paid the rent up front), we resigned ourselves to a two-hour round trip each day, just to get to work.

Des muttered under his breath but took this latest cock-up in his stride. To make matters worse, it started to rain quite heavily and the work was less than exciting – stripping out and shredding several acres of umbrella trees which were growing out of control and threatened to choke everything around them.

Umbrella trees, or *schefflera actinophylla* to give them their Latin name, are native Australian plants. They are often grown in tropical and sub-tropical gardens, and flourish as houseplants in temperate climates. However they also hitch a lift, so to speak, on the trunks of other trees in rainforests or – in this case – woodland, and once established, often grow as high as 50 feet. Hence the need to chop them down before they get out of control.

Despite the weather, travel and rather tedious work, I thoroughly enjoyed this week because my companions were all hardworking and co-operative and I knew I could go back to my 'home-from-home' at the end of the day.

Although I had opted out of camping, I still helped to prepare and wash up the evening meal, in order not to seem too aloof. I was rewarded one evening when a spectacular green meteor shot horizontally across the sky. The event was sufficiently rare to make one of the local TV news bulletins that night.

The final night, it was Nam Pyo's twenty-second birthday so I was sent off to find a cake for him in the local Woolworths, as well as 22 candles.

Koreans love photographing themselves and each other, using the 'V' for peace sign as a mandatory pose for each picture. Instead of everyone taking pictures at the same time, Nam Pyo was forced to re-light and blow out the candles six times as his fellow Koreans took their individual pictures. The result was a virtually inedible cake with a thick layer of candle wax icing.

Furthermore, Nam Pyo's friends had insisted on buying the meat for our final barbecue but were clearly not familiar with Australian butchery. Thus we sat masticating barbecued stewing steak and particularly fatty belly pork, which they had carefully chosen for the occasion.

The next morning, I got out of bed at 0600 and staggered over to the caravan site to help everyone pack up, even though I had decided to stay on in Noosa for a couple of days in order to visit Frazer Island. This is the world's largest sandbar, some 90 miles long, but it still manages to sustain a massive rain forest and is a world heritage site.

The unseasonal rain had finally eased and the good weather had returned. We took down the tents, stowed away everything in the trailer and made our farewells with much exchanging of email addresses and promises of visits to London, Seoul, Tokyo and Paris.

I then decided to walk through Noosa National Park which, despite being our original destination, I had never actually visited. I walked for three hours along the coastal path and then into the heart of the park.

The month had often been tiring, sometimes boring, occasionally irritating, and frequently uncomfortable. But the fact remained that I had kept up with the other volunteers who were all younger than my own children, and with a few notable exceptions, I had found them interesting and good company. The admirable Des had hugely enhanced my time as a volunteer and I had visited places, met people and seen wildlife that I would normally never have encountered.

But above all, I continued my 20-year love affair with Australia. OK, there are things I don't like about Oz, not least its ambivalent attitude towards aborigines. I attended a rally in Melbourne on *National Sorry Day*, when, in theory, the nation is supposed to apologise to native aborigines for the way they have been treated. As virtually all the crowd in Federation Square was of aboriginal descent, with barely a white face to be seen, it was difficult to take this act of contrition very seriously.

Nonetheless, this booming, in-your-face, spectacularly beautiful country had come an incredibly long way in a very short space of time. And what other country would have a shopping mall with a Salvation Army thrift shop, flanked either side by a sex boutique and a maternity wear outfitters?

Above all, Australians enjoy gently poking fun at anyone who comes from elsewhere on the planet. For example, a Texan farmer goes to Australia for a vacation. There he meets an Aussie farmer and gets talking. The Aussie shows off his big wheat field and the Texan says, "Oh! We have wheat fields that are at least twice as large".

Then they walk around the ranch a little, and the Aussie shows off his herd of cattle. The Texan immediately says, "We have longhorns that are at least twice as large as your cows."

The conversation has, meanwhile, almost died when the Texan sees a herd of kangaroos hopping through the field. He asked, "And what are those?"

The Aussie replies with an incredulous look: "Don't you have any grasshoppers in Texas?"

Conclusion

I hope this book will have provided some inspiration or, at the very least, given you some amusement and/or interest.

I have been surprised by the extent to which my relatively mild heart problems have affected my life. Apart from swallowing bucket loads of pills every day – not to mention having enough blood tests to sate Dracula's thirst – it is hard not be reminded that I have suddenly changed from being a normal healthy person into someone who is deemed to 'have a heart problem'.

For several months after my heart attack, I used to tidy out cupboards and frenetically clean behind the fridge, because I kept imagining that I could hear the 'tut-tuttings' from my daughters as they sorted out my affairs after my death.

When I recently cashed in a pension, I was offered an increased settlement because I was considered to have an 'impaired' life: i.e. with any luck, the pension company wouldn't have to pay out for very long.

Of course, in reality, I am probably more likely to die from being knocked over by a car than from another heart attack or from a stroke, particularly as I now have a pretty normal and active life.

The difference from my pre-heart attack era, however, is that I now need reassurance on a regular basis that I am really okay, and that I am not about to have an unwanted chat with the Grim Reaper.

I do believe that mildly adventurous and active travel is the best way I know of providing that reassurance and, perhaps more importantly, giving my heart the exercise it badly needs. If you are now in reasonable heath again too, or even if you still suffer from various heart problems, I want to encourage you to take your heart on at least one interesting journey, provided that you take reasonable care and sensible precautions. If you do, I am sure that you will feel a lot calmer, fitter and thus happier on your return. Good luck and bon voyage.

And again, please feel free to share your own experiences on www.travelswithmyheart.com.

Part Three

Heart Searching

A. SPECIALIST TOUR OPERATORS, VOLUNTARY WORK HOLIDAYS AND TRAVEL OPPORTUNITIES TO RAISE MONEY FOR CHARITIES

Much as I would have liked to sample the wares of all the holiday companies, volunteer organisation and charities listed below, neither time nor finances have allowed. So I have culled basic details about a pretty broad selection of them from brochures, websites recommendations from friends and lots of telephone conversations with the companies and organisations themselves.

However, you should interrogate your proposed tour operator, volunteer body or charity about the level of fitness required and if you are in doubt, ask if you can be put in touch with one of its clients who has done the particular trip or activity you are interested in. You may get that dreary old 'Data Protection Act' line, but if the organisation really want your custom, it will contact appropriate clients to get their permission for you to speak to them.

I have graded the specialist tour operators into budget, medium and expensive but this has been done on a rough and ready basis to give you an idea of the type of holiday they are offering.

1. SPECIALIST TOUR OPERATORS

Activities Abroad

Active multi-activity holidays designed for families, in coastal and mountain Europe and Turkey. Mostly water based, with walking, climbing and canyoning.
Family focus gives these holidays flexibility and guaranteed supervision and safety with trained local providers. A pulse rating indicates the degree of action and courage needed. Positive attitude

rather than peak fitness is recommended. Cuisine is local and accommodation comfy but not four star, as the brochure sensibly warns you. Pricing is linked to the number of activities chosen.

www.Activitiesabroad.com
Tel: 01670 789991
Suite 2, Netherton Park, Stannington,
Northumberland NE61 6EF
info@activitiesabroad.com   **Medium/Budget**

The Adventure Company

Wildlife, landscape, cultural, family activity and escorted adventure holidays in small groups.

The Adventure Company offers escorted trips to remote untouched places, 'providing a balance of well-known highlights and places off the beaten track'. There's a mixture of activities – walks, treks, sightseeing – and travel in small groups of like-minded people. All ages welcomed but core group is 25–55. No single supplements! Accommodation generally 'small, clean, family-run tourist class hotels' but also more basic off-the-beaten-track type accommodation, depending on the trip. There are six grades between gentle and strenuous. Most trips are described as 'more demanding than mainstream travel', mainly because of high temperatures, method of travel or unfamiliar customs, rather than because of physical demands.

www.adventurecompany.co.uk
Tel: 0845 4505316
Cross & Pillory House, Cross & Pillory Lane, Alton GU34 1HL
Sales@adventurecompany.co.uk   **Medium**

Archipelago Azores

Small group, independent and family walking, cycling and whale-watching tours.

Offers small and independent tours tailored to your own interests. Cycling holidays are graded 'easy' to 'strenuous'.

www.Azoreschoice.com
Tel: 017687 75672
1b Museum Square, Keswick, Cumbria CA12 5DZ
Info@azoreschoice.com   **Medium/Expensive**

Andrew Weir Shipping

Manages the RMS St Helena – the only route to St Helena.

Offers a variety of packages including sailings to South Africa and Namibia. There are some UK/St Helena trips. If you are on a tight budget, there are some lower fares in a four-berth cabin but they are very small.

> ***www.aws.co.uk***
> Tel: 020 7575 6480
> Dexter House, 2 Royal Mint Court, London EC3 N4XX
> *Reservations@aws.co.uk*   **Medium/Expensive**

Voyages also available through:

> Strand Voyages, 1 Adam Street, London WC2N 6AB
> Tel: 020 7766 8225 *Voyages@Strandtravel.co.uk* or
> The Cruise People, 88 York Street, London W1H 1QT
> Tel: 020 7723 2450 *cruise@dial.pipex.com*

Body And Soul

Health, beauty, fitness, taichi, yoga and other gentle activity holidays.

Run by the long-established Erna Low, it offers a wide range of treatments in spas all over the world as well as various sporting activities. Aimed at those who want to be pampered. Even includes 'anti-tobacco' treatment. Many of its programmes include a 'medical consultation' – this is generally a fairly brief check-up to ensure that you are in general good health, as there are some treatments that should not be taken if you are suffering from certain medical conditions such as high blood pressure. The medical consultation will also give you the option of explaining what you would like to get out of your treatment programme, so that the doctor can tailor the programme for your particular requirements.

> ***www.Bodyandsoulholidays.com***
> Tel: 020 7594 0290
> 9 Reece Mews, London SW7 3HE
> *spas@ernalow.co.uk*   **Expensive**

Dragoman Overland

Overland travel on four continents.

Group holidays aimed at introducing the traveller to the unusual and tucked away and has an emphasis on participating. Holidays include escape, discover, encounter, family and 'ultimate'.

www.Dragoman.com
Tel: 01728 862217
Camp Green, Debenham, Stowmarket, Suffolk IP14 6LA
sales@dragoman.co.uk   **Medium**

Equine Adventures

Horse riding, wildlife, walking and diving in France, Ireland, Iceland, Africa, Middle East, Asia, Americas.

Riding range includes centre based, trail, safari, pack and working ranch. Tours graded from 'beginner' to 'experienced' in a very wide range of interesting places you'd be unlikely to discover for yourself. Small print spells out the fitness and medical certificates required, and reminds travellers that it is not an ordinary travel operator, and that flexibility about itineraries may be needed. Small groups, mostly up to 12, many smaller, and in Iceland up to 20.

www.equineadventures.co.uk
Tel: 0845 1306981
Long Barn South, Sutton Manor Farm, Bishop's Sutton, Alresford, Hants SO24 OAA
sales@equineadventures.co.uk   **Medium/Expensive**

Exodus

Multi-activity worldwide. Walking, trekking, cycling, overland, winter, water.

Walking options range from those for the occasional walker to the experienced enthusiast. Small groups up to 16, expert leader, porterage and seven grades of challenge. Versatile mix of ages (av. 39), genders, singles, couples, groups. Cycling holidays include self-guided, road and off road trips graded easy, moderate, strenuous and demanding, with assurance that you don't need to be a bike fanatic. Except self-guided, experienced leaders are with you as are support vehicles. Accommodation is in hotels, lodges or camping. There are also various trekking holidays.

www.exodus.co.uk
Tel: 0870 9500039
Grange Mills, Weir Road, London SW12 0NE
Sales@exodus.co.uk   **Medium/Budget**

Explore!

Worldwide trips, walking treks, family adventures, cycling and short breaks.
Pioneers of original small group adventure holidays for over 25 years.
Tours are designed to 'get you closer to different people, cultures and
landscapes'. You can choose from over 300 small group tours to
more than 130 countries. 40 active family adventures are on offer, as
well as walking & trekking holidays to discover remote cultures and
the world's greatest landscapes. Also short adventure breaks for 4-6
days and small group cycling tours.

> ***www.explore.co.uk***
> Tel: 0870 3334001/2
> Explore Worldwide Ltd, Nelson House, 55 Victoria Road,
> Farnborough GU14 7PA
> *res@explore.co.uk*   **Medium**

Guerba

*Worldwide accompanied overland adventure, safari and walking options,
especially Africa. Groups of 10–22 and customized tours. Nature, history,
culture tours, all graded.*
Started as an overland to Africa company, now very experienced with
trips in 50 countries across six continents with many single travellers.
Trips from 4 to 24 days. The company offers a sense of adventure, but
aims for the trips to be 'hassle' free and for you to experience the
environment; the six difficulty grades help you choose what suits you
ranging from 5 which is *tough but rewarding* down to grade 1 which
involves no strenuous activity. European options are now included
and you can learn Spanish with a local family too.

> ***www.Guerba.com***
> Tel: 01373 826611
> Guerba World Travel Ltd, Wessex House, 40 Station Road,
> Westbury, Wilts BA13 3JN
> *Res@guerba.co.uk*   **Budget but doesn't include
>   travel to start point**

Headwater

*Guided and independent winter sports, walking and cycling holidays mostly
in Europe. Also some in the Eastern Mediterranean, North Africa, Latin
America and Caribbean.*

Well planned and supported activity holidays, to be taken in small groups or independently but usually meeting up with other travellers in especially chosen hotels each evening. An easy to follow one/two/three boots (or cycles) ratings system should ensure the right ratio of effort to enjoyment. Good backup for all activities and well informed, usually local guides.

www.headwater.com
Tel: 01606 720033
The Old School House, Chester Road, Northwich, Cheshire CW8 1LE
info@headwater.com   **Medium**

Inntravel

Pampered, easy-going cycling and walking in Europe.
Well planned holidays for independent cyclists and walkers with all the practical arrangements taken care of and back up support for you, and of course the bicycles. Food and hotels chosen for quality and comfort. Lots of flexibility to customize aspects of the trip: e.g. to upgrade a hotel. Brochure gives three grades for walking and details ascents/descents and distances. Cycling not graded but described as 'gentle and relaxed'.

www.inntravel.co.uk
Tel: 01653 617949
Nr Castle Howard, York YO60 7JU
Cycling@inntravel.co.uk   **Medium/Expensive**

Jubilee Sailing Trust

Adventure sailing holidays for able-bodied and disabled people.
A UK-based charity that aims to promote the integration of able bodied and disabled people through adventure sailing holidays. The JST welcomes people from all over the world on its two specially designed tall ships, *The Lord Nelson* and *Tenacious*.

www.jst.org.uk
Tel: 0870 4435781
Hazel Road, Woolston, Southampton SO19 7GB
info@jst.org.uk   **Budget**

KE Adventure Travel

Adventure holidays to distant places including trekking, touring, safari and climbing for the very fit only. Mountain biking also included.

Main focus trekking in small (max 16), looked-after groups in Europe, Turkey, south and east Asia – including Nepal, India, Bhutan, Tanzania, S America, Morocco. Trips range from seven days in Europe to month-long expeditions. Some tours graded easy are for 'most people in good health', so anyone with heart problems should discuss with KE and their own doctor before booking – there's detailed information on physical demands on website. Vegetarian catered for and possibility for other diets. Range of comprehensive and helpful brochures with different foci.
See also:

KE Adventure Biking in Europe, Africa, Asia, the Americas.
Small group biking adventures, graded moderate – challenging – severe.
Distances vary between 30 and 100 km daily. Easier options in Cuba, Slovakia, Turkey. See above for health issues.

www.Keadventure.com
Tel: 017687 73966
32 Lake Road, Keswick, Cumbria CA12 5DQ
info@keadventure.co.uk   **Budget**

The National Mountain Centre

Mountaineering and hill walking courses in Snowdonia.
Offers a wide range of outdoor activities, some of which are suitable for those with heart conditions.

www.pyb.co.uk
Tel: 01690 720214
Plas y Brenin, Capel Curig, Conwy LL24 OET
info@pyb.co.uk   **Budget**

Peregrine Adventures

Antarctica and the High Arctic adventures on special cruise ships. Also nature, hiking, kayaking, walking, trekking, wilderness and small group adventure travel worldwide including Himalayas, Europe, Africa. Some less active culture, wildlife and history trips.

Environmentally responsible company with a range of adventure travel options in all continents. Comfortable private transport with all costs up front. Ages 30–70. Antartic/arctic exploration in comfortable cruise ships with experts on board, carrying 110–120, and exploring according to interest. Smaller sized interest groups formed according to interest and 'designed to accommodate varying levels of physical activity'. This could include hiking, snow shoeing, camping, kayaking, plus photography, ornithology. Also walking, trekking, wilderness (and some cycling) options range in challenge from reasonably active to needing 'mental challenge and physical stamina'. All ages in mind, clear descriptive grading to guide choice includes information about physical challenge and type of accommodation which can include camping and be basic. Groups of 10–15 with experienced leaders.

www.peregrineadventures.co.uk
Tel: 0844 7360170
1st Floor, 8 Clerewater Place, Lower Way, Thatcham, Berks RG19 3RF
sales@peregrineadventures.co.uk   **Medium/Expensive**

Ramblers

Small group (all accompanied) and independent walking tours; Europe and worldwide.

A long-standing (60 years) outdoor activity company, offering walking, trekking, skiing, exploring and sightseeing. Those over 75+ won't feel isolated and the company is adding holidays for the under 40s. Clearly graded to suit all levels from 'easy' to 'pioneer'. Many options cater for a couple of levels. Also special focus groups including photography and ancient history.

www.ramblersholidays.co.uk
Tel: 01707 331133
Lemsford Mill, Lemsford Village, Welwyn Garden City, Herts AL8 7TR
info@ramblersholidays.co.uk   **Budget/Medium**

Sailing Holidays

Flotilla sailing in the Aegean for the less experienced sailor.
Independent, flotilla, courses and independent combined, or 'pot luck' options, which include 'learn to sail' or 'improver' courses held around the Aegean from April to October. The company says that

the Aegean is one of the 'most safe and stable sailing environments in the world'. Total beginners are catered for but the clear and sensible brochure points out the value of any outdoor and/or water based familiarising activity. Very experienced leaders and skippers ensure safety.

www.sailingholidays.com
Tel: 020 84598787
105 Mount Pleasant Road, London NW10 3EH
mail@sailingholidays.com **Medium**

STA Travel

Company with a huge range of possibilities in terms of place, length of stay, degree of comfort, physical challenge.
Too many to list but, for example, varied options in Africa include *Young at Heart* for over 50s, diving, overland safaris and *Access Africa* for 'the physically challenged' – 4 days to 46; lodges, tents, treks, culture focus, safari, city breaks and coastal, desert and mountain tours. Costs (core cost, plus mandatory and optional local payments) clearly set out with further summary of what is and isn't included, e.g. travel, sleeping bags. No grading as such but *Is it for You* gives sound guidance on what might suit you and has additional questionnaire for over 40s.

www.statravel.co.uk
Tel: 0871 2300040
1st Floor, 135 Notting Hill Gate, London W11 3LB
e-mail via web site **Budget/Medium**

Sundowners

Overland – sights, culture and adventure in Asia. Small groups.
Highly regarded Asia Overland travel company offering the most extensive choice of overland journeys across Asia. Over 40 years of continued success is due to a focus on Asia and the quality of the journeys and experiences they provide.

www.sundownerstravel.com
Tel: 020 88777660
Suite 207B, The Business Village, 3-9 Broomhill Rd., London SW18 4JQ
Europe@sundownerstravel.com **Medium**

Sunvil

Mostly Greece, some Albania. Bookable water based activities and walking. Package and independent holidays.

'Good quality holidays away from the mainstream'. Varied options include hotel, villa, self-catering and multi centre. Opt for walking, cycling, scuba diving and other active options in places all over the Greek mainland and islands. Learn to sail with Sunvil sailing, or hire skippered or non-skippered yachts.

    www.Sunvil.co.uk
    Tel: 020 8568 4758
    Sunvil House, Upper Square, Old Isleworth, Middx. TW7 7BJ
    Greece@sunvil.co.uk   **Budget/Medium**

Terracotta Trails

Cooking & walking in Italy. Self-guided and personalised.

Self-guided holidays allow you to set your own pace as you walk along the trails of the Monti Sibillini National Park and the surrounding area. You overnight in the medieval town of Spoleto before setting off for a week's walking in the Apennine mountains. Welcoming family-run hotels await you and there is the chance of a day off with a pool to enjoy.

    www.terracottatrails.com
    Tel: 0208 1441237
    Terracotta Trails Ltd, Lartons Mill House, Lower Kilcott,
    Hillesley, Glos GL12 7RC
    Info@terracottatrails.com   **Medium**

TrekAmerica

Small group adventure in North and Central America for all ages.

30 year-old TrekAmerica runs small group adventure holidays. In addition to summer treks, there is a wide range of camping, lodging, walking, biking & family adventure tours for all ages throughout USA, the Canadian Rockies, Alaska, Mexico, Belize & Guatemala. It also operates small group adventures in Central & South America including Costa Rica, Ecuador, Galapagos, Peru, Bolivia, Chile, Argentina and beyond, as well as sixteen different camping & lodging tours across Australia & New Zealand exploring the outback, beaches, reefs, mountains & cities.

www.footloose.com
Tel: 0870 4448735
TrekAmerica Travel Ltd, 16/17 Grange Mills, Weir Road,
London SW12 0NE
Sales@trekamerica.co.uk   **Budget/Medium**

Waymark

Active tuition holidays in Europe.

Activities with tuition. In the winter these include downhill and
cross-country skiing, snowshoeing and mixtures are offered in small
accompanied groups, often in hotels and guesthouses where
everyone sits down together. Grades are from 1 (beginners or
improvers) to 4 (strenuous). For summer walking and trekking, grade
one is about four hours walking with limited ascent, to grade four,
seven hours with some scrambling. The brochure sensibly points out
that 'normal good health' is essential for all active holidays. Different
levels often accommodated on the same holiday, and 'time out' is
easily built in.

www.waymarkholidays.com
Tel: 0870 9509800
First Choice House, London Road, Crawley, West Sussex
RH10 9GX
Enquiries@waymarkholidays.com   **Medium**

West Somerset Railway

*Longest working steam passenger heritage railway in the UK. Runs a variety
of courses for those wanting to learn to drive a steam engine.*

Offers a range of one- and two-day courses 'to realise your ambition
to drive a railway engine and to make long-held dreams a reality'.
The Steam Engineman Courses are designed for moderately fit men
and women over 18 and will teach you the principles of working a
steam locomotive, signalling, braking, safety, driving and firing.

www.West-Somerset-Railway.co.uk
Tel: 01643 704966
The Railway Station, Minehead, Somerset TA24 5BG
info@West-Somerset-Railway.co.uk   **Budget**

2. VOLUNTARY WORK HOLIDAYS/ ASSIGNMENTS

British Trust for Conservation Volunteers

A charity supporting practical conservation work by volunteers throughout Britain.

It supports many local groups across the country, runs training courses, and organises working holidays. BTCV is a great way to get experience of the conservation industry and many full time workers started off volunteering for it. Also markets working holidays in Europe and further afield.

> ***www.bctv.org***
> Tel: 01302 388888
> Sedum House, Mallard Way, Potteric Carr,
> Doncaster DN4 8DB
> *Information@btcv.org.uk*

Conservation Volunteers Australia

A not-for-profit organisation that offers a number of different volunteer opportunities from one day local environmental projects through to two week expeditions to remote outback locations for working holiday experience.

Has offices in Ballarat, Melbourne, Geelong, Bendigo, Sydney, Bathurst, Newcastle, Port Macquarie, Canberra, Wollongong, Adelaide, Alice Springs, Darwin, Perth, Broome, Hobart, Launceston, Brisbane, Gladstone, Townsville, Mackay and Cairns and projects are geographically linked and managed from, these centres. Very popular with young people from South Korea and Japan. Its mission is to attract and manage a force of volunteers in practical conservation projects for the betterment of the Australian environment. Founded in 1982 in Ballarat, Victoria, it employs more than 120 full time staff. Has a handful of UK agents but it would seem to be cheaper to book direct on its web site.

> ***www.conservationvolunteers.com***
> Tel: 0061 35 3302660
> Greenhill Enterprise Centre, Cnr University Drive /Enterprise Grove, Mount Helen, VIC 3350, Australia
> *Postal address*: Box 423, Ballarat, VIC 3353, Australia
> *Info@conservationvolunteers.com.au*

Coral Cay Conservation

Tropical forest and coral cay conservation in the Caribbean and Asian-Pacific.
International community-based tropical forest and coral cay
conservation group with David Bellamy as president. There's no
upper age limit and most groups tend to consist of a good mixture of
ages – it's for 'career break, gap year, retirement or holiday'. You
don't need to be a specialist; after training, you collect baseline
ecological data to help survey and monitor the natural environment.
Minimum commitment two weeks. If you are a member of the
society, you can also join their expedition trips.

> *www.coralcay.org*
> Tel: 0207 620 1411
> 1st Floor Block 1, Elizabeth House, 39 York Road,
> London SE1 7NJ
> *Info@coralcay.org*

Cross Cultural Solutions

*An American-based organisation offering volunteering opportunities for one to
twelve weeks with two hundred annual start dates with no formal application
process.*
Operates international volunteer programmes in partnership with
sustainable community initiatives, bringing people together to work
side-by-side while sharing perspectives and fostering cultural
understanding. No specific qualifications or experience are required;
your volunteer abroad placement is based on your particular skills
and interests. CCS welcomes a wide range of participants to its
programmes including families and groups.

> *www.crossculturalsolutions.org*
> Tel: 0845 4582781/2782
> Tower Point 44, North Road, Brighton BN1 1YR
> *Infouk@crossculturalsolutions.org*

John Muir Trust

*Offers adventurous activities and exploration in wild areas of Scotland
including canoeing and sea kayaking trips, conservation work, wilderness
skills etc.*
The John Muir Trust was formed in 1983 to protect and conserve
wild places in Scotland and to increase awareness and understanding

of them. The activities and conservation programme offers volunteers the opportunity to help carry out conservation work in places such as Ben Nevis.

> **www.jmt.org**
> Tel: 0131 554 0114
> 41 Commercial Street, Edinburgh EH6 6JD, Scotland
> *Admin@jmt.org*

Médecins du Monde

An international humanitarian aid organisation. See also under Charities.
Recruits medical and non-medical volunteers who provide healthcare for vulnerable populations around the world.

> **www.medecinsdumonde.org.uk**
> Tel: 020 7516 9103
> 34th Floor, One Canada Square, Canary Wharf,
> London E14 5AA
> *info@medecinsdumonde.org.uk*

National Trust

The National Trust runs around 450 working holidays every year throughout England, Wales and Northern Ireland.
Working holidays range from two to seven days and include food and hostel-type accommodation. No previous experience is necessary, as trained volunteer leaders and staff will lead you. You just need to be team-spirited, enjoy being outdoors in beautiful locations and not mind getting your hands dirty. Have to book up to a year ahead to get onto a weekend break – whole weeks are easier.

> **www.nationaltrust.org.uk**
> Tel: 01793 817400
> National Trust Central Volunteering Team, The National
> Trust, Heelis, Kemble Drive, Swindon SN2 2NA
> *Volunteers@nationaltrust.org.uk*

Pueblo Inglés

A language school in Madrid that recruits volunteers to hold conversation classes with Spaniards for a week in hotels in rural locations in exchange for free board and lodging.
Unlike other volunteering opportunities, this is run purely as a

business and Spaniards pay large sums to take part. However it is an interesting way to meet a wide range of people as the volunteers come from all over the world and accommodation and food are pretty good.

www.morethanenglish.com
Tel: 0034 91 391 34 00
Rafael Calvo 18, 4th floor, 28010 Madrid, Spain
anglos@puebloingles.com

Real Africa Excursions

Volunteering trips to Uganda and Kenya.
Claims to 'stretch you both physically and emotionally'. It offers to groups of 12–14 an introduction to the 'real' Africa including meeting people in their homes, eating their food, hearing their music, listening to their stories and working with them. There is also the opportunity to watch wildlife. All visitors who travel or work with Real Africa projects in Uganda, or anywhere else they operate, do so on equal terms irrespective of disability.

www.real-africa.co.uk
Tel: 01363 83957
15 Moorland View, Lapford, Nr Crediton, Devon EX17 6OA
e-mail via web site

Real Gap Experience

Offers hundreds of real gap year and career break adventures covering thirty countries and providing opportunities to travel, work abroad, volunteer with communities, children and wildlife and learn new skills.
Has several options including paid work, although this almost certainly would not apply to over 26s because of visa restrictions. Offers volunteering assignments including research work with people, animals and conservation projects. Also has a subsidiary called **Gap Year For Grownups**.

www.realgap.co.uk
Tel: 01892 701881
First Floor, No.1 Meadow Road, Tunbridge Wells,
Kent TN1 2YG
Info@realgap.co.uk

Responsibletravel.com

An online travel agent, based in Brighton, launched in 2001 for travellers who want holidays that also benefit the environment and local people.

Markets charity treks, community projects, family volunteering, footpath repair, habitat conservation, marine conservation, rainforest work, teaching, Tsunami support & volunteering, turtle, wildlife conservation and wolf conservation. It claims to market carefully pre-screened holidays from over 270 leading worldwide tourism brands and businesses. The *Independent* says: 'As every member of the Green Set will tell you, the key travel agent is responsibletravel.com'.

> *www.responsibletravel.com*
> Tel: 01273 600030
> 4th Floor, Pavilion House, 6 Old Steine, Brighton BN1 1EJ
> *Amelia@responsibletravel.com*

Saga Volunteer Travel

New Saga initiative for the over 50s – chance to add on volunteering to a Saga holiday or travel solely for volunteering. Initial projects are only in South Africa.

Volunteer experiences vary from a week to three months and will offer something for all travellers, whether they come to a project with specific skills or simply have the desire to put something back into the local communities in destinations that host Saga holidaymakers.

SVT says that everyone can make a valuable contribution as long as they have an open mind and willing spirit. It offers to give you the opportunity to travel and meet new cultures, share and develop your skills, assist local communities in need and maybe even learn a little more about yourself.

> *www.saga.co.uk/travel*
> Tel: 0800 0156981
> The Saga Building, Middelburg Square, Folkestone, Kent CT20 1AZ
> *Reservations@saga.co.uk*

Voluntary Service Overseas

The best known charity for sending volunteers to developing countries. It only send qualified people on long-term assignments: it is definitely not a volunteering holiday organisation.

The average age of a volunteer is 38 and most placements are for two years. It is the leading development charity with almost 2,000 skilled professionals currently working in over 40 countries. VSO responds to requests from governments and community organisations throughout Asia and Africa.

The volunteers aim to pass on their expertise to local people so that when they return home their skills remain. Volunteers can be aged between 20 and 75 years old and must have a formal qualification and some work experience.

www.vso.org.uk
Tel: 020 8780 7200
317 Putney Bridge Road, London SW15 2PN
Infoservices@vso.org.uk

3. TRAVEL OPPORTUNITIES WITH CHARITIES

Across the Divide
Walk, cycle, climb across the world in 'open' charity events.
ATD organises charity challenges across the world, for example off the beaten track to Machu Picchu, climbing Kilimanjaro, dog-sledding in Norway, Vietnam cycle challenge, etc. The company claims that its staffing ratios are the highest of any provider for this type of trip, so adventure comes with the highest standards of safety.

www.acrossthedivide.com
Tel: 01460 30456
Jubilee House, Fore Street, Thorncombe, Nr Chard, Somerset TA20 4PP
Events@acrossthedivide.com

Discover Adventure Ltd
Organised trips worldwide for charity of your choice – cycle or trek. Trips include China, Morocco, Iceland, Vietnam, and UK. Around 8–18 days.
All trips (moderate, tough and extreme) are designed to provide a physical challenge for which you need to train. Company says even moderate trips are not easy – you need to be able to walk or cycle for

eight hours a day. Travelling is in small groups, usually camping, sometimes-traditional hotels and sharing. Luggage is transported for you. Ages range from 18–70 from all walks of life. Fundraising and payment options available. A fundraising target of £2000 is usually required.

www.discoveradventure.com
Tel: 01722 718444
Throope Down House, Blandford Road, Coombe Bissett, Salisbury, Wilts SP5 4LN
Info@discoveradventure.com

Global Vision International

Volunteer projects (2 weeks to a year) worldwide.
GVI promotes sustainable development through research, education and direct financial support, working closely with local partners. Volunteers – who should be 'adventurous individuals' – can join expeditions or projects in the fields of research, conservation and education. These have included turtle protection (Panama), working with indigenous children (Guatemala) and teaching in Nepal. No experience is necessary. Ages 18–65. Expeditions (e.g. Costa Rica, Amazon, Mexico) 5 to 15 weeks.

www.gvi.co.uk
Tel: 0870 6088898
GVI UK Office, 3 High Street, St. Albans, Herts AL4 8EJ
Info@gvi.co.uk

Medecins du Monde

Medical humanitarian aid organisation. Asia, Africa and in London and Paris. Walking/trekking/cycling events. Also provides opportunities for medical volunteers on its projects.
Charity providing medical care to vulnerable populations with medical and non-medical volunteers. Fund raising events have included a Sahara trek, and a London to Paris bike ride. Also recruits paid volunteers with medical training.

www.medecinsdumonde.org.uk
Tel: 0207 5169103
Medecins du Monde UK, 29th Floor, One Canada Square, London E14 5AA
Info@medecinsdumonde.org.uk

Moderate, challenging and extreme treks and moderate cycling events world-wide and Europe.

The Children's Society employs specialists tour operators for their far-flung trip options in for example – Vietnam, South Africa and India as well as walks in New York and Newcastle on Tyne. All ages take part and at different fitness levels. TCS provides training advice. Trek group size is between 20–50 people though the average is 30–40.

> ***www.childrenssociety.org.uk***
> Tel: 0845 3001128
> Edward Rudolf House, Margery Street, London WC1X 0JL
> *Supporteraction@childrensociety.org.uk*

4. USEFUL TRAVEL WEBSITES

www.activehotels.com

An excellent and easy-to-use site for every type of independent hotel ranging from small hotels, guest houses and B&Bs to the most upmarket hotels. A real rival to the corporate chains.

www.adventuredirectory.com

This website is perfect for those looking for adventure. It has masses of links to thrill-seeking holiday sites and you can search for your trip by activity or destination.

www.airlinequality.com

This site makes fascinating if scary reading with airline and airport rankings, seat pitch guide, best seats and above all, user comments about virtually every airline in the world. When you have read some of these, you will want to give many airlines a very wide berth!

www.ba.com

British Airways is now as hooked on selling directly on the web as Easyjet and Ryanair. Easy to use site and always worth consulting – it is often cheaper than buying from the multitude of low-cost air fare websites.

www.britishairways.com/travel/healthintro/public/en_gb
This website, produced by British Airways, provides health and medical information for planning, during and after a flight. It offers advice on fitness to fly, specific medical conditions, flying when pregnant, fear of flying, travel immunisations, medical care in the air, cabin air quality, deep vein thrombosis (DVT) and jet lag. There is also information about the British Airways Travel Clinics including locations and appointments, products and services.

www.bbc.co.uk/health/healthy_living/travel_health
A very useful website with a wide variety of health information relating to travelling at home and abroad. As the site says: 'Whether you're trekking through the mountains of Nepal or cavorting in a caravan at Clacton, you can make sure your holiday goes with a swing by incorporating some advance planning.' Here the Beeb gives you a helping hand.

www.bootsnall.com
A travel blog with loads of interesting stories and useful information as well as masses of web links.

www.cheapflights.co.uk
One of the first internet travel websites, it compares the prices of different airlines and tour operators and publishes over a million deals for comparison each day.

www.couchsurfing.com
Perhaps not for older readers, but this site offers couch swapping as opposed to house swapping. A risky but cheap option.

www.cybercafes.com
Has details of internet cafes all over the world.

www.dh.gov.uk/PolicyAndGuidance/HealthAdviceForTravellers /fs/en
This website provides health advice for travellers and is made available by the Department of Health (DH). Aimed at UK residents travelling overseas, it provides information and advice on topics

covering food, sun exposure, insect and animal bites, swimming, care on the roads, hazardous sports and diving, personal hygiene, alerts on outbreaks of major diseases all over the world, an immunisation checklist, health insurance, and reciprocal health care agreements.

www.easyjet.com
The future's definitely very orange with Easyjet. Easy to use site but can have irritating glitches with credit card payments and logging in. But at those prices, who can grumble?

www.embassyworld.com
A directory and search engine for the world's embassies and consulates.

www.expedia.com
Originally owned by Microsoft, now the biggest in the business, selling competitive package deals as well as flights, hotels, etc.

www.eurostar.com
Many people with heart conditions would rather not fly and you are able to book trains from London through to Paris, Lille and Brussels and various other destinations at different times of the year on this pretty efficient website. An easy change at Lille also gives you access to the whole TGV network in France.

www.fitfortravel.scot.nhs.uk/
Fit for Travel is the NHS website providing travel health information for those travelling abroad from the United Kingdom. Content on this site is compiled and maintained by staff from the Travel Medicine Division at the Scottish Centre for Infection and Environmental Health (SCIEH). Apart from general travel health advice this resource provides travel health advice for special groups such as pregnant travellers, the disabled, the elderly and children. There is a facility to search the site by either map, region or an A to Z index for particular vaccine and malaria recommendations. Current news items covering outbreaks and topical subjects can be found in the Extra Notes section.

www. hostelz.com
The ultimate international hostel guide and booking engine. It tells it

as it is, which may stop you landing up in a real flea pit.

www.igluski.com

An internet-based travel agency specialising in the sale of ski and
snowboarding holidays, villa holidays, tropical holidays and city
breaks. It offers ski holidays to Europe and North America. The web
site features useful ski tips, fitness advice, snow reports, last minute
holiday deals, news etc.

www.lastminute.com

lastminute.com was launched in 1998, to sell unsold holidays,
flights, accommodation etc. at the last minute. Recently bought
out by Travelocity which has caused confusion and some
glitches.

www.laterooms.com

This site will find you a bed when all others are full up and it always
offers very cheap prices.

www.lonelyplanet.com

Masses of useful information as you would expect but I took its
recommendation on a hotel in Madrid and thought it was nowhere
near as good as LP claimed, with possibly the world's smallest
bedroom. Lonely Planet also now has its own TV channel
(**www.lonelyplanet.tv**) and a hotel booking service.
(**www.haystack.lonelyplanet.com**).

www.madadventure.com

Although mainly aimed at young people, the site does say it is getting
more applications from older people, though I suspect we are talking
thirties and forties rather than senior citizens. Madventure offers
community development projects and adventures worldwide. The
website is well-designed and there would seem to be some vetting
before you are assigned a project, unlike some other more
commercially oriented operations.

www.opodo.com

This website belongs to the major airlines including British Airways,

Air France and Lufthansa. It now sells holidays, hotel rooms and seats on virtually every airline.

www.organicplacestostay.co.uk
A useful site for the organically minded, but strongest on UK and European accommodation. Has links to information on more far flung places.

www.priceline.co.uk
Brings the concept of bid-up TV and eBay (where you can also buy holidays) to buying hotel rooms on the internet. You name a price and if it's within the acceptable range, that's what you pay. You can save up to 50%.

www.raileurope.co.uk
This site enables you to book all sorts of rail tickets and passes for most corners of Europe.

www.ryanair.com
Like its feisty boss, you expect this website to punch you in the face if you don't follow its rules. Will take you to places you have never heard of and never realised you wanted to visit at sometimes knock-down prices. But beware – get it right first time, as Ryanair is unforgiving about changes and refunds.

www.seatguru.com
Legroom is vital for anyone at risk of a DVT – and that includes many people with heart conditions. This site gives detailed seat-plan graphics which show which seats have limited recline, reduced legroom or a headrest video screen.

www.seat61.com
Run by a real rail junkie called Mark Smith, this site tells you pretty well everything you need to know about booking train tickets across Europe and throughout the world.

www.skicentral.com
A directory of ski and snowboard related sites. Features a search

engine that provides keyword searching and an extensive knowledge base. The web site includes over 2,000 hotels, lodges and condos and thousands of packages from over 43 tour operators to choose from.

www.skyscanner.net
Compares all the low-cost carriers across a simple table and tells you where the cheapest fares are in Europe and which destinations are the cheapest from any European airport.

www.snowlife.org.uk
Shops, brands, dry slopes, tuition, travel agents, clubs and schools.

www.thomsonfly.com
Lots of cheap flights but a very irritating site which doesn't always work very well.

www.thorntree.lonelyplanet.com
Named after a cafe in Nairobi where travellers tacked messages to each other on the notice board, it is still a great place to get advice on all aspects of travel.

www.timeanddate.com
Very handy website giving current time, date, dialing codes, etc. for most of the world's major cities.

www.Traveldodo.com
A new website which aims to collect "dos' and 'don'ts' travel tips from all over the world.

www.travelocity.com
Much plugged by Alan Whicker in TV advertising, it has a useful flexible search tool if you are not committed to a particular day but the site can be confusing since it bought lastminute.com.

www.travel-quest.co.uk
A specialist holiday and travel directory with endless ideas for activity and adventure holidays. It also offers links to sports breaks, adventure and special interest holidays from independent specialist holiday companies – in the UK, Europe, North America and worldwide.

www. travel.roughguides.com
The website of the incomparable *Rough Guide* travel books. If you register, you can make contact with other travellers.

www.tripadvisor.com
Now the biggest repository of unbiased reader reviews (although owned by Expedia so I use the word unbiased with caution), covering more than 200,000 hotels and attractions.

www.tripprep.com
Loads of information about travel medicine and practitioners all over the world.

www.virtualtourist.com
A global community of 750,000 members who have contributed over three million travel tips and 2.5 million photos covering 25,000 locations worldwide. As it links every comment to a member's profile, you can meet those who have posted travel reviews.

www.whats–on–guide.co.uk
A useful site for finding on what is going on all over the UK – perfect for adding some pleasure to your pain!

www.whatsonwhen.com
This worldwide events guide will help you structure your travels around the top festivals, exhibitions and carnivals all over the world.

www.who.int/en
This World Health Organisation website gives up to date information on health problems/scares around the world and offers advice on inoculations, etc.

www.worldwikia.com
Run by the same people behind wikipedia.org, anyone can write and edit travel reviews on any destination in the world. It also picks up content from commercial travel websites.

www.xe.com
An excellent website for checking exchange rates and converting currencies from virtually every country around the globe.

5. GOOD HOTELS FOR WALKERS IN UK

A hard day's walking is a lot less painful if you know you are going to get a good meal and a comfortable bed at the end of the day. *The Good Hotel Guide* lists a number of hotels and bed and breakfasts that fit the bill. I have picked out a number of entries in a few prime walking areas, but the list is by no means comprehensive.

I have not included prices as they get out of date very quickly, but a phone call or a visit to the hotel web sites will tell you what you need to know. Better still – buy the guides.

I have also included some hotels from by the incomporable Harden's guide database, although the publisher has no currrent hotel guide in print.

The Peak District

Baslow Hall
Calver Road, Baslow DE45 1RR
Tel: 01426 583259 *www.fischers-baslowhall.co.uk*
Peacefully situated on the edge of the Chatsworth Estate, this quite formal country house is a great location for exploring the Peak District. (*Harden's*)

Biggin Hall
Biggin-by-Hartington, Buxton, Derbyshire SK17 0DH
Tel: 01298 84451 *www.bigginhall.co.uk*
There are footpaths in all directions over beautiful countryside from or near the grounds of this unpretentious small hotel. (*The Good Hotel Guide*)

Underleigh House
Hope, Derbyshire S33 6RF
Tel: 01433 621372 *www.underleighhouse.co.uk*
Within the Peak District national park, Philip and Vivienne Taylor's long, low, creeper-covered conversion of a Victorian barn and cottages has good walking from the door. They 'point you in the right direction' with maps and packed lunches. (*The Good Hotel Guide*)

Amerdale House

Arncliffe, BD23 5QE

Tel: 01756 770250 *www.amerdalehouse.co.uk*

This fabulous, quietly located, family-run country house hotel is a welcome retreat in a lovely part of the Yorkshire Dales and handy for walking. (*Harden's*)

The Burgoyne Hotel

Reeth, near Richmond, DL11 6SN

Tel: 01748 884292 *www.theburgoyne.co.uk*

Compasses and detailed maps are given to walkers at this Grade II listed Regency house on the green of a village in the Yorkshire Dales. (*The Good Hotel Guide*)

Moorlands Country House

Levisham, Pickering YO18 7NL

Tel: 01751 460229 *www.morlandslevisham.co.uk*

A converted vicarage with limited rooms but unlimited charm, service and meal quality. There are many walks locally and also bridleways. Even stabling is available. (*Harden's*)

Shallowdale House

West End, AmpleforthYO62 4DY

Tel: 01439 788325 *www.shallowdalehouse.co.uk*

On a sheltered slope of the Hambleton Hills, Phillip Gill and Anton van der Horst's small guesthouse is just within the North Yorks Moors National Park (with 1,400 miles of paths and tracks). (*The Good Hotel Guide*)

The Sportsman's Arms

Wath-in-Nidderdale, near Harrogate, North Yorkshire HG3 5PP

Tel: 01423 711306 *www.sportsmans-arms.co.uk*

Reached across an old packhorse bridge over the River Nidd, it is popular with locals, walkers, birdwatchers and fisher folk. (*The Good Hotel Guide*)

Borrowdale Gates

Grange-in-Borrowdale, CA12 SUQ
Tel: 0870 06787 *www.borrowdale-gates.com*
This hotel can feel a bit Spartan if you visit off-season but the
cooking is exceptional and is particularly recommended for walkers.
(*Harden's*)

Bridge

Buttermere, Cockermouth CA13 9UZ
Tel: 01768 770252 *www.bridge-hotel.com*
A chintzy hotel in an 18th century building that has a wonderful
location in the fells *(Harden's)*

Hazel Bank

Rosthwaite, near Keswick CA12 5XB
Tel: 017687 77248 *www.hazelbankhotel.co.uk*
In an area 'hard to beat for a walker', Glen and Brenda Davies's small
hotel in Borrowdale has wonderful views of the mountains. (*The
Good Hotel Guide*)

Kirkstone Pass Inn

Kirkstone Pass, LA22 0JZ
Tel: 01534 33624 *www.geocities.com/kirkstonepassinn*
The highest pub in the Lakes is a get-away-from-it-all destination
par excellence, detached even from the National Grid (though it
does have a generator). Warm and welcoming. (*Harden's*)

The Leathes Head Hotel

Borrowdale, Keswick, Cumbria CA12 5UY
Tel: 017687 77247 *www.leatheshead.co.uk*
Roy and Janice Smith offer 'warm and personal service' at their
gabled Edwardian house, high up in wooded grounds outside
Borrowdale – 'a perfect and relaxed hotel for walkers'. Mrs Smith, a
qualified physiotherapist, 'will soothe aching muscles and joints'. (*The
Good Hotel Guide*)

The Mill Hotel

Mungrisdale, Penrith CA11 0XR
Tel: 017687 79659 *www.themillhotel.com*
In a hamlet at the foot of mountains, this 17th-century former mill
cottage, still with millrace, waterfall and trout stream, is seconds from
a footpath through 'lonely, wild countryside towards Blencathra, one
of the great peaks'. (*The Good Hotel Guide*)

Old Dungeon Ghyll

Great Langdale, near Ambleside, LA22 9JY
Tel: 015394 37272 *www.odg.co.uk*
This 'unique Victorian mountain hotel' has long welcomed fell
walkers and serious climbers. Owned since 1928 by the National
Trust, and run since 1983 by Neil and Jane Walmsley, it is in a green
valley on the approach to England's highest mountain, Scafell Pike.
(*The Good Hotel Guide*)

Old Rectory

Torver, near Coniston, LA21 8AX
Tel: 015394 41353 *www.theoldrectoryhotel.com*
'Such good value for money.' Paul and Elizabeth Mitchell's 19th-
century building stands in gardens and woods beneath the peaks of
Coniston Old Man; many bedrooms have wide views. (*The Good
Hotel Guide*)

Seatoller House

Borrowdale, Keswick, CA12 5XH
Tel: 017687 77218 *www.seatollerhouse.co.uk*
At the head of the beautiful Borrowdale valley, this 350-year-old
building is an unpretentious guesthouse. It is much liked by hikers
and ramblers for its homely atmosphere, camaraderie and good value.
(*The Good Hotel Guide*)

Wasdale Head Inn

Wasdale Head, near Gosforth, CA20 1EX
Tel: 019467 26229 *www.wasdale.com*
This three-gabled inn, seven miles up a dead-end road, has
mountains on three sides. Owned by Kate and Howard Christie, it is

popular with climbers and hikers. The inn has its own microbrewery. (*The Good Hotel Guide*)

The West Country

Gurnard's Head
Treen, Zennor, St Ives TR26 3DE
Tel: 01736 796928 *www.cornwall-online.co.u/gurnards-head/*
A superb location close to the coastal walk are the virtues of this traditional Cornish country pub with food. (*Harden's*)

Porlock Vale House
Porlock Weir, Somerset TA24 8NY
Tel: 01643 862338 *www.porlockvale.co.uk*
This 'easy-going' sporting hotel is well known in equestrian circles, but non-horsy visitors can enjoy good walking. The South West Coast Path runs along the boundary and Helen and Kim Youd provide leaflets of other suggested walks. (*The Good Hotel Guide*)

Lydgate House
Postbridge, Dartmoor, Devon PL20 6TJ
Tel: 01822 880209 *www.lydgatehouse.co.uk*
There is good walking from the door at Peter and Cindy Farrington's Victorian country house. It is 'very special, when the wind howls, and the fog is over the moor.' (*The Good Hotel Guide*)

Scotland

Airds
Port Appin, Argyll PA38 4DF
Tel: 01631 730236 *www.airds-hotel.com*
'Walking is perhaps the main pastime in the area,' say Shaun and Jenny McKivragan, former guests who returned to buy this old ferry inn. Local walks include the 40-minute Clach Thoull circular route, which starts at the front door; the more adventurous head for Glencoe. (*The Good Hotel Guide*)

Balcary Bay

Shore Road, Balcary Bay, Auchencaim,
Castle Douglas DG7 1QZ
Tel: 01556 640217 *www.balcary-bay-hotel.co.uk*
A country house hotel that's tipped in particular for its delightful
peaceful location, overlooking the sea and surrounded by gentle
walks. (*The Good Hotel Guide*)

Hilton Craigendarroch

Braemar Road, Ballater AB35 5XA
Tel: 01339 755858 *www.hilton.com*
Lovely location, good leisure facilities and good walks with a golf
course nearby – the quality of the catering, though is a let-down.
(*Harden's*)

Inverlochy Castle

Torlundy, Fort William PH33 6SN
Tel: 01397 702177 *www.inverlochycastlehotel.com*
Very very expensive (e.g. £350 for a single room in high season) but
of exceptionally high quality, in the foothills of Ben Nevis with a
wonderful warm welcome. (*Harden's*)

The Old Mill Highland Lodge

Talladale, Loch Maree, Ross-shire IV22 2HL
Tel: 01445 760271 *www.theoldmillhighlandlodge.co.uk*
There is superb hill walking in this isolated and wild corner
of Wester Ross. Chris and Joanna Powell's purpose-built Highland
Lodge has a 'wonderful' view of the peak of Slioch. (*The Good Hotel
Guide*)

Wales

Bell at Skenfrith

Skenfrith, Monmouthshire NP7 8UH
Tel: 01600 750235 *www.skenfrith.co.uk*
Lovely food and idyllic surrounding with lots of nice walks – it also
has great location by a ruined castle. (*Harden's*)

Clytha Arms

Clytha, NP7 9BW
Tel: 01873 840206 *www.clytha-arms.com*
Very good food and A1 wines are the particular draw to this country
pub with a few rooms in good walking country. (*Harden's*)

Lake Vyrnwy

Lake Vyrnwy, Llanwddyn SY10 0LY
Tel: 01691 870692 *www.lakevyrnwy.com*
Fairytale views from the lakeside bedrooms and the restaurant are the
highlights at this very comfortable hotel. It is set in a large estate,
which offers some great walks. (*Harden's*)

Maes Y Neuadd

Talsarnau, Gwynedd LL47 6YA
Tel: 01766 780200 *www.neuadd.com*
Everything is perfect in this partly 14th century building with a very
good restaurant, views of Snowdonia and excellent walking and
sightseeing. (*Harden's*)

Pen-y-Gwryd

Nant Gwynant, Gwynedd LL55 4NT
Tel: 01286 870211 *www.pyg.co.uk*
Brian and Jane Pullee's inn at the foot of Snowdonia is not for
everyone, but those who love it really love it. Popular with
mountaineers, it was the training base for the 1953 Everest
expedition. The Pullees insist on 'proper behaviour: no baseball caps
indoors, no drinking straight from a bottle'. (*The Good Hotel Guide*)

References

*Harden's Guides, 14 Buckingham Street, London WC2N 6DF (Tel: 0207
839 4763 www.hardens.com)*

*The Good Hotel Guide, Great Britain and Ireland, 50 Addison Avenue,
London W11 4QP (Tel: 020 7602 4182; www.goodhotelguide.com).*

6. SPECIALIST WALKING TOUR OPERATORS

You will find a surprising number of walking tour operators but many of them are very small – effectively one man bands who make some money out of their enthusiasm.

I think this list is pretty comprehensive although no doubt there are some others lurking out there that I haven't discovered.

About Argyll Walking Holidays

Guided walking/hiking holidays in the Southwest Highlands and Islands of Scotland. Small groups (8 maximum).

Letters Lodge South, Strathlachlan, Argyll PA27 8BZ, Scotland
Tel: 01369 860272 *www.aboutargyll.co.uk*

Adventureline

Specialises in Cornwall. Small groups with max of nine.

North Trefula Farm, Redruth, Cornwall TR16 5ET, UK
Tel: 01209 820847 *www.adventureline.co.uk*

Anglesey Walking Holidays

Self-guided walking holidays along the 125 Coastal Path. Pre-arranged accommodation, transport, luggage transfer. Personal service by local couple, with supply of maps, route planners etc. Tailor made, with optional rest days.

3 Penrallt, Menai Bridge, Isle of Anglesey LL59 5LP
Tel. 01248 713611 *www.angleseywalkingholidays.com*

Bath West Walks

Guided and self-guided walking holidays exploring the Cotswolds, Exmoor, Somerset & Wiltshire. Among the places visited are Bath, Avebury, Bourton on the Water, Glastonbury, Stonehenge & Wells.

Osmington, Brewery Lane, Holcombe, Bath BA3 5EG
Tel: 01761 233807 *www.bathwestwalks.com*

Bespoke Highland Tours

Walking packages which include selected accommodation and daily baggage transfers in the Western Highlands and Islands. Long distance trails and location based holidays.

Tigh Na Creig, Garve Road, Ullapool, Ross-shire IV26 2SX
Tel: 01854 612628 *www.highland-tours.co.uk*

Byways Breaks

Gentle cycling, walking and cottage holidays in Shropshire and
Cheshire and along Offas Dyke path. Comfortable accommodation
and flexible routes exploring quiet countryside, small villages, castles,
pubs and tea-rooms. Full support including luggage transfer.

25 Mayville Road, Liverpool L18 0HG
Tel: 0151 722 8050 *www.byways-breaks.co.uk*

Celtic Trails

Walking holidays in Wales. Guided and independent, walking with
baggage transfer. Cycling holidays in Wales, Offas Dyke Path,
Pembrokeshire Coastal Path, Cambrian Way, Snowdonia Trail, Lleyn
Coastal Path, Glyndwrs Way, Wye valley walk, Pilgrim Trail,
Mawddach Estuary, Dovey Valley Way.

PO Box 11, Chepstow NP16 6DZ, Wales, UK
Tel: 0800 9707585 *www.celtrail.com*

City of London Walks

Walking tours in the City of London, with trained City Guides and
Clerkenwell guides specialising in more out of the way nooks and
crannies, the origins of the tales and the people of London.

Contact by e-mail only *cityoflondonwalks@blueyonder.co.uk*
www.cityoflondonwalks.co.uk

Coast to Coast Holidays

Coast to coast walking holidays, door-to-door luggage transfers and
cycle transportation. Flexible and personal service.

60 Durham Rd, Redcar, Cleveland TS10 3RY
Tel: 01642 489173 *www.coasttocoast-holidays.co.uk*

Contours Walking Holidays

Guided walking holidays (hiking tours) and unguided hikes in the
UK – Scotland, England and Wales.

Gramyre, 3 Berrier Road, Greystoke CA11 OUB
Tel: 017684 80451 *www.contours.co.uk*

Cotswold Walking Holidays

A range of guided and self guided walking holidays in the Cotswolds.

Festival House, Jessop Avenue, Cheltenham, Glos GL50 1RL
Tel: 01242 633680 *www.cotswoldwalks.com*

Discerning Traveller

Leisurely self-guided walking tours in England, Wales and Scotland. Specialists for Cornwall, Cotswolds, Lake District, Pembrokeshire Coast.

24 Cardigan Street, Oxford OX2 6BP
Tel: 01865 515618 *www.discerningtraveller.co.uk*

Discovery Travel

Run by cyclists and walkers, so strong on their needs. Walking Holidays include Wainwright's Coast to Coast Walk, the Cumbria Way, Dales Way and Cleveland Way.

Opsa House, 5a High Overgate, York Y01 8ZZ
Tel: 01904 632226 *www.discoverytravel.co.uk*

European Mountain Tours

Provides walking holidays with qualified guides to mountains in the UK, including the Lake District, Snowdonia, and all over Scotland. Also offers walking trips in continental Europe.

Address withheld
Tel: 01539 565 818 *www.european-mountain-tours.co.uk*

Explore Britain Walking Holidays

Walking, cycling and sailing in England, Scotland, Wales and Ireland.

6 George Street, Ferryhill, Co. Durham DL17 ODT
Tel: 01740 650900 *www.xplorebritain.com*

Footpath Holidays

Offers guided walking and hiking tours throughout Great Britain.

16 Norton Bavant, Nr Warminster, Wiltshire BA12 7BB
Tel: 01985 840049 *www.footpath-holidays.com*

Foot Trails

Guided walking breaks in Wiltshire and Dorset. Choose from walks exploring Wiltshire's medieval past, Stonehenge and Avebury Stone circles or Stourhead Gardens.

2 Underdown Mead, White Road, Mere, Wiltshire BA12 6EX
Tel: 01747 861851 *www.foottrails.co.uk*

HF Holidays

Provides guided and independent walking holidays in the UK,
Europe and around the world.

Imperial House, The Hyde, Edgware Road, London NW9 5AL
Tel: 020 89059558 *www.hfholidays.co.uk*

High Trek Snowdonia

Guided & self guided trekking holidays in North Wales (week-long
luggage transported). Long weekend courses & breaks in climbing,
scrambling, navigation, Welsh 3000's, hill walking, mountain
adventure, winter skills etc.

Tal y Waen, Deiniolen, Gwynedd LL55 3NA
Tel: 01286 871232 *www.hightrek.co.uk*

Hillscape Walking Holidays

Self-guided walking holidays from 3-star guest house in rural Mid-
Wales. 40 day walks to choose from, 5–20 miles in length,
throughout the Cambrian Mountains and Ceredigion Heritage
Coast.

Hillscape, Blaen-y-ddôl, Pontrhydygroes, Ystrad Meurig SY25 6DS
Tel: 01974 282640 *www.wales-walking.co.uk*

Laidback Trailblazers

Walking holidays in Cornwall and 'taster' bed & breakfast breaks.
Coastal Paths – Cornish Bays including St. Ives, Lamorna; Minack
Theatre Breaks; Gardens (Eden, Heligan, Trebah, Tresco); Heritage,
Mining & Saints Trail.

The Old Barn, Bosulval, Newmil, Penzance TR20 8XA
Tel: 01736 367742 *www.laidback-trails.co.uk*

Lancaster Authentic

Escorted hiking & walking vacations in rural Britain.

Stoneridge House, 9 Cromwell Road, Lancaster LA1 5BD
Tel: 01524 67007 *www.lancasterauthentic.com*

Lightfoot Walking Holidays

Unescorted walking holidays along the Cornish Coastal Path. Accommodation arranged and luggage transported all the year round.

Lightfoot Nanquitho, Calloose Lane, Leedstown, Hayle, Cornwall TR27 5ET Tel: 01736 850715 *www.lightfootwalkingholidays.co.uk*

Marches Walks

Tailor-made guided walking holidays in the Marches of England and Wales, Wye valley and surrounding area.

Footsteps, Cwmbach, Glasbury-on-Wye, Powys HR3 5LT Tel: 01497 847149 *www.marches-walks.co.uk*

Merseyventure

Travel and transfer service for walking groups wishing to attempt the National Three Peaks Challenge of Ben Nevis, Scafell Pike and Mount Snowdon.

Contact by e-mail: *richie@merseyventure* *www.merseyventure.com*

Mickeldore Travel

Individually tailored walking and cycling holidays in Northern England.

14 Manor Park, Keswick CA12 4DE Tel: 017687 72335 *www.mickledore.co.uk*

Northwest Walks

Inn-to-inn guided walking holidays on the Coast to Coast trail, the Cumbria Way and the Dales Way.

16 Langham Rd, Standish, Wigan WN6 Tel: 01257 424889 *www.north-west-walks.co.uk*

Rob Roy Tours

Specialist for walking and activity holidays (language learning, golf, cycling, painting). Incentives, sightseeing tours in Scotland, England and Wales and Scottish heritage tours.

630 Lanark Road, Juniper Green, Edinburgh EH14 5EW Tel: 01620 890908 *www.robroytours.com*

Safe Journeys

Walking holiday treks in Perthshire, Scotland, including The Rob

Roy Way. Also features guided treks in Nepal.

Old Crieff Road, Aberfeldy, Perthshire PH15 2DH
Tel: 01887 820143 *www.safejourneys.co.uk*

Sherpa Expeditions

Worldwide walking and cycling holidays from a comprehensive
selection of escorted or self-guided departures to destinations around
the world.

131a Heston Road, Hounslow TW5 0RF
Tel: 020 8577 2717 *www.sherpa-walking-holidays.co.uk*

Sherpa Van Project

Provides a back-up service for walkers and cyclists following long
distance foot trails and cycle ways in Britain. Baggage moved door to
door from hotels or B&Bs.

29 The Green, Richmond, North Yorkshire DL10 4RG
Tel: 0871 5200124 *www.sherpavan.com*

Skye Walking Holidays

Based at Duntulm Castle Hotel, on the northern most tip of the
Trotternish peninsula, on the Isle of Skye. Accommodation provided is
either hotel based or self catering coastguard cottages. Walking holidays
can be guided or independent, and can also have one of the following
themes: Wildlife, Heritage, Gaelic Music or Whisky. Other activities
include cycling, kayaking, pony trekking and dinghy sailing.

Duntulm Castle Hotel, Duntulm, Isle of Skye IV51 9UF
Tel: 01470 552213 *www.skyewalks.co.uk*

Southern Upland Way

A comprehensive source of information available to assist with
planning a walking holiday across Scotland's coast to coast as well as
shorter walking holidays in Southern Scotland.

26 Main Street, Dalry, Castle Douglas DG7 3UW
Tel: 0870 8358448 *www.southernuplandway.com*

The Life of Riley

Walking holidays in England and Spain – including Brontë Country
and Sierra Nevada.

Apartado de Correos 88, 18420 Lanjaron, Granada, Spain
Tel: 0034 696 354 824 *www.thelifeofriley.eu.com*

Tracks Walking Holidays

Self-guided walking holidays throughout Scotland, on all the long
distance paths and many others off the beaten track.

26 Forbes Road, Edinburgh EH10 4ED
Tel: 0131 229 6844 *www.maketracks.net*

Transcotland

Walking holidays with arrangements for accommodation, baggage
transfer and route information. Independent walking holidays
includes West Highland Way and Coast to Coast.

5 Dunkeld Road, Aberfeldy, Perthshire PH15 2EB
Tel: 01887 820848 *www.transcotland.com*

UK Exploratory

Offering self-guided walking holidays in the UK, the West Highland
Way, Lake District and the Isle of Skye.

9 Copperfield St, Wigan WN1 2DZ
Tel: 01942 826270 *www.alpineexploratory.com*

Walkabout Scotland

Walking holidays, day tours and weekend breaks in the Scottish
Highlands and Lowlands in small 'sociable' groups. Fully guided.

70 Strathearn Road, Edinburgh EH9 2AF
Tel: 0845 686 1344 *www.walkaboutscotland.com*

Walk Awhile

Offers a range of walking holidays in the heart of the Kent
Countryside.

Montgreenan, St Catherine's Drive, Faversham, Kent ME13
Tel: 01227 752762 *www.walkawhile.co.uk*

Walking Breaks

Self-guided supported walking tours of Suffolk Heritage Coast &
Constable Country. The coastal tours are linear along a waymarked
trail and use hotels noted for their comfort and food. The tours of

Constable Country and The Wool Towns are circular in nature and use a mix of hotels, village inns and historic guesthouses. Luggage transfers are included in the prices.

Bradfield Hall Barn, Alder Carr Farm, PO Box 82, Needham Market, Suffolk IP6 8BW
Tel: 01449 721555 *www.walkingbreaks.com*

Walkingworld

Downloadable Ordnance Survey maps and step-by-step instructions for walks all round the UK. Database of walks growing daily, all submitted by local people.

Tufton Lodge, Barras, Kirkby Stephen, Cumbria CA17 4JD
Tel: 017683 42029 *www.walkingworld.com*

Wandering Aengus Treks

Trecks include the three highest peaks of Scotland, England and Wales within a fully inclusive, guided holiday.

Fellside End, Fellside, Cumbria CA7 8HA
Tel: 016974 78443 *www.wanderingaengustreks.com*

Wayfarers

Walking vacations in England, France, Italy, Scotland, Ireland, Wales, Switzerland, the United States and New Zealand.

7 The Square, Toddington, Glos GL54 5DJ
Tel: 01242 620871 *www.thewayfarers.com*

Way2go4 Walking Holidays

Guided walking holidays on the North Devon and Cornwall Border aimed at those who enjoy relaxed walking.

Home Farm, Welcombe, Devon EX39 6HH
Tel: 01288 331416 *www.way2go4.com/walking*

Weekenders

A relaxed walking holiday in the heart of Devon run by Mark Ashley for up to six guests.

Russetts, Halsfordwood Lane, Nadderwater EX4 2LD
Tel: 01392 811481 *www.devonweekenders.co.uk*

Westcountry Walking Holidays

Guided and self-guided walking holidays covering South West Coast Path, Exmoor, Dartmoor and Lundy Island.

55 The Quay, Clovelly, Bideford, Devon EX39 5TF
Tel: 0845 094 3848 *www.westcountry-walking-holidays.com*

Wild Adventures

A range of walking, biking, cycle touring, camping and winter skills/mountaineering holidays throughout the Highlands and Island of Scotland.

The Bothy, Skye of Curr, Dulnain Bridge, Inverness-shire PH26 3PA
Tel: 01479 851374 *www.wild-adventures.co.uk*

Wild Rover Tours

Guided hiking tours in the Mourne Mountains, County Down, Northern Ireland.

24 Kinghill Avenue, Newcastle, County Down BT33 0RU
Tel: 0284 3722186 *www.discovernorthernireland*

Wild Wales

Climbing courses and outdoor weekends in Snowdonia, North Wales; walking and hiking in the hills and mountains, climbing and scrambling, botanical holidays, Celtic history weekends and map reading courses.

1 Trecastell Terrace Henryd, Conwy, North Wales LL32 8EZ
Tel: 01492 582 448 *www.wild-wales.co.uk*

Wilderness Scotland

Small group walking holidays in the most remote regions of Scotland. Guided and self-guided options available, as are other adventure activities.

3A St Vincent Street, Edinburgh EH3 6SW
Tel: 0131 625 6635 *www.wildernessscotland.com*

will4adventure

UK and worldwide treks, hill skills, rock climbing and mountaineering courses, Challenge 4 Charity, free walking weekends etc.
Contact by e-mail *will@will4adventure.com* *www.will4adventure.com*

Wight Walks

Self led independent walking holidays on the Isle of Wight.

22 Broadfields Avenue, Cowes, Isle of Wight PO31 7UD
Tel: 01983 281662 *www.wight-walks.co.uk*

This directory has been partly assembled with information from
www.britainexpress.com

7. CYCLING WEBSITES

National

CTC
Has a useful mapping project for CTC members to share their
routes. Click on "Cycle A-way" to download existing route
PDFs.
www.ctc.org.uk

Cycle Maps
A wonderfully simple directory of hundreds of printable cycle maps.
www.cyclemaps.org.uk

Everyday Cycling
Impressive routes and rides section with suggestions for circular
routes to suit all abilities across Britain.
www.everydaycycling.com

Sustrans
Allows you to search a route location and displays National
Cycle Network routes in this area. Hard-copy maps available to
order.
www.sustrans.org

The Forestry Commission
Boasts more than 1,600 miles of off-road cycling trails in forests
throughout Britain.
www.forestry.gov.uk

The National Byway
Promotes cycling along Britain's heritage routes.
www.thenationalbyway.org

Waterscape
Details an impressive number of lovely cycling routes around the
British canal network.
www.waterscape.com

Scotland

Cycling in Scotland
Definitive guide to Scotland's cycle paths and mountain bike trails.
www.visitscotland.com

Cycle Hebrides
This site will help you plan your trip entirely, from routes to
accommodation.
www.cyclehebrides.com

Ride Fort William
Details trails and terrain to suit all abilities.
www.ridefortwilliam.co.uk

Upper Deeside Access Trust
More than 50 downloadable route maps for covering the beautiful
glens of Deeside.
www.visitdeeside.org.uk

Wales

Cycling North Wales
Illustrated cycle route maps for North Wales, on- and off-road.
www.cyclingnorthwales.co.uk

Cycling Wales
This site lists cycling breaks and tour operators in Wales.
www.cycling.visitwales.com

Mountain Biking Wales
Excellent site featuring the latest mountain biking trails and news.
www.mbwales.com

Northern Ireland

Cycle Northern Ireland
A definitive guide – all levels of trips and routes are listed here, from the laid-back to the hardcore.
www.cycleni.com

Discover Northern Ireland
Broad range of information, from guided city tours to major and minor trails across the counties, all available on downloadable PDFs. Just input the keyword Cycling.
www.discovernorthernireland.com

The Causeway Coast
Information about the 14 routes in this region.
www.causewaycoastandglens.com

England

Cycle Wight
Offers a number of cycle-friendly routes on the Isle of Wight.
www.cyclewight.org.uk

Devon Cycling
Information about commuter, leisure and national cycle routes, cycle hire and accommodation.
www.devon.gov.uk/cycling

Hampshire Council Cycling
Easy-to-use website dedicated to Hampshire's 750 miles of cycle routes. Includes downloadable leaflets for every trail.
www.hants.gov.uk/cycling

Transport for London

Comprehensive website offering security and maintenance advice, 19 borough cycling maps (which can be ordered free of charge) and an excellent advanced journey planner with downloadable maps.
www.tfl.gov.uk

Holiday ideas

B&B Cycling Guides

Lists the best cycle-friendly B&Bs on Britain's well-known long-haul cycle routes.
www.coast-and-castles.co.uk

Bicycle Beano

Vegetarian cycling breaks in Wales.
www.bicycle-beano.co.uk

Carefree Cycling

Offers a range of services, from days out and tours abroad to weekend breaks and cycle dating.
www.carefreecyclingtours.co.uk

Cotswold Country Cycles

Discover Shakespeare country by bike on these bespoke routes.
www.cotswoldcountrycycles.com

Cycle Holidays

An impressive directory of cycling holidays the world over.
www.cycle-holidays.co.uk

CTC Cycling Holidays

Offshoot of the CTC organisation, allowing you to look at global holiday options month by month.
www.cyclingholidays.org

Discovery Travel

Organise guided tours on Britain's most famous long-distance routes.
www.discoverytravel.co.uk

European Bike Express

This company collects holiday-goers and their bikes and drops them off at one of 12 points on a Mediterranean cycle route.
www.bike-express.co.uk

European Cyclists' Federation

News on all things bike related in Europe, plus hundreds of holiday tours and destinations.
www.ecf.com

Exodus

Arranges worldwide cycling holidays with itineraries to cater for all abilities.
www.exodus.co.uk

Hooked On Cycling

Offers specialist road-cycling holidays. Book a pre-planned journey or customise your own.
www.hookedoncycling.co.uk

With many thanks to **The Guardian** *which compiled this list for a special cycling supplement.*

8. HEART-FRIENDLY INSURANCE COMPANIES

Below is a list of some insurers who specialise in pre-existing medical conditions. On random like-for-like quotes, their prices seem to vary enormously. For example, when trying to cover for two weeks to the USA, I was quoted anywhere between £150 and £750! So try them all (however tiresome and time consuming) or contact a specialist broker.

Please note that these companies are not listed on merit.

Able2Travel

Tel: 0870 7506711 *www.able2travel.com*

Specialist insurance brokers. Every case is treated individually, taking into account both the medical condition and the intended holiday, including area to be visited and length of stay etc. Occasionally underwriters do require increased policy excesses due to a particular condition but premiums remain the same, regardless of the medical problem. Won't cover over 80s.

All Clear Travel Insurance
Tel: 0870 7779339 *www.allcleartravel.co.uk*
Insurance especially designed for travellers with medical conditions. Cancer and other serious conditions are all considered even if a terminal prognosis has been given. No age limits and usually no doctor's certificate is needed. Cover can be arranged in one phone call or online. Nearly all applicants covered. No proposal form required.

Free Spirit Travel Insurance
Tel: 0845 230 5000 *www.free-spirit.com*
Specialist travel insurance for people with pre-existing medical conditions. You can also buy online from this site.

Freedom Travel Insurance
Tel: 0870 774 3760 *www.freedominsure.co.uk*
Covers pre-existing conditions including viruses. Medical screening required.

It's So Easy Travel Insurance
Tel: 0845 222 4205 *www.itssoeasytravelinsurance.com*
Simple telephone medical screening process. Offers annual policies. Charitable organisation linked to Freedom to Travel.

J.D. Consultants
Tel: 01689 859102 no website
Insures people with a variety of pre-existing conditions including haemophilia and viruses. Telephone medical screening required.

Right Cover Travel Insurance
Tel: 0870 850 1284 *www.rightcovertravelinsurance.co.uk*

Not a specialist insurance company for serious existing medical conditions but is prepared to consider covering those with them on a case by case basis and makes a point of saying so.

The Insurance Surgery
Tel: 0870 458 7955 *www.the-insurance-surgery.co.uk*
Specialist insurance brokers for clients with existing conditions.
They claim to do the searching for you although you have to make the calls.

The British Heart Foundation will also give you a list of heart-friendly insurers but I found, incongruously, that some of them wouldn't cover people with heart conditions!

9. ORGANISATIONS OFFERING HELP TO PEOPLE WITH HEART PROBLEMS

American Heart Association
National Center, 7272 Greenville Avenue, Dallas TX 75231
Tel: 0011 301 223 2307
Email via website
www.americanheart.org

Anticoagulation Europe
P O Box 405, Bromley BR2 9WP
Tel: 020 8269 6875
anticoagulationeurope@ntlworld.com
www.anticoagulationeurope.org

Arrhythmia Alliance
PO Box 3697, Stratford Upon Avon, Warwickshire CV37 8YL
Tel: 01789 450787
info@arrhythmiaalliance.org.uk
www.arrhythmiaalliance.org.uk

The Aviation Health Institute
17c Between Towns Road, Oxford OX4 3LX

Tel: 01865 715 999
info@aviation-health.org
www.aviation-health.com

British Cardiac Patients Association
2 Station Road, Swavesey, Cambridgeshire CB4 5QJ
Helpline: Tel: 01223 846845
Tel: 0800 479 2800
enquiries@bcpa.org.uk
www.bcpa.co.uk

British Heart Foundation
14 Fitzhardinge Street, London W1H 6DH
Helpline: Tel: 08450 70 80 70
Administration: Tel: 020 7935 0185
Email via website
www.bhf.org.uk

British Heart Foundation Scotland
Ground Floor, 4 Shore Place, Edinburgh EH6 6UU
Tel: 0131 5555891
scotland@bhf.org.uk

British Heart Foundation Wales
21 Cathedral Road, Cardiff CF11 9HA
Helpline: Tel: 0870 6006566

Cardiac Risk in the Young (CRY)
Unit 7, Epsom Downs Metro Centre, Waterfield, Tadworth,
Surrey KT20 5LR
Tel: 01737 363222
cry@c-r-y.org.uk
www.c-r-y.org.uk

Cardiomyopathy Association
40 The Metro Centre, Tolpits Lane, Watford,
Hertfordshire WD18 9SB
Tel: 01923 249977

info@cardiomyopathy.org
www.cardiomyopathy.org

Chest Heart and Stroke Scotland
65 North Castle Street, Edinburgh EH2 3LT
Tel: 0131 225 6963
admin@chss.org.uk
www.chss.org.uk

Heart UK
7 North Road, Maidenhead, Berkshire SL6 1PE
Tel: 0845 4505988
ask@heartuk.org.uk
www.heartuk.org.uk

MASTA
Medical Advisory Service for Travellers Abroad
Moorfield Road, Yeadon LS19 7BN
Tel: 0906 8224100
enquiries@masta.org
www.masta-travel-health.com

The Heart Failure Foundation
Crest House, 7 Highfield Road, Edgbaston, Birmingham B15 3ED
Tel: 0212 4564188
contactus@heartfailurefoundation.org
www.ahf.org.uk

Tourism for all
The Hawkins Suite, Enham Place, Enham Alamein, Andover,
Hants SP11 6JS
Information: Tel: 0845 1249971
info@tourismforall.org.uk
www.tourismforall.org.uk

10. OTHER USEFUL ADDRESSES

The Association of British Travel Agents
68–71 Newman Street, London W1T 3AH
Tel: 020 7637 2444
abta@abta.co.uk
www.abta.com
Foreign & Commonwealth Office
Whitehall, London SW1A 2AL
Tel: 020 72701500
Travel information: 0845 850 2829
www.fco.gov.uk
Also FCO dedicated web site for those going on gap year.
www.GoGapYear.com

Nomad Travel Stores and Clinics
Travel health information line: 09068 633414
orders@nomadtravel.co.uk
www.nomadtravel.co.uk